From Your Friends At **The MAILBOX®** *Magazine*

TRACE & LACE, COLOR & PASTE

FINE-MOTOR ACTIVITIES FOR LITTLE HANDS

PRE-K GRADE 1

WRITERS:
Bonnie Cave, Judy Huskins, Sandy McNeil

PRODUCT DEVELOPMENT MANAGER:
Kathy Wolf

EDITOR:
Ada Hamrick

COPY EDITORS:
Carol Rawleigh, Gina Sutphin

ILLUSTRATORS:
Jennifer T. Bennett, Cathy Spangler Bruce, Cathie Carter, Donna Teal

COVER DESIGN:
Jennifer T. Bennett

TABLE OF CONTENTS

PART ONE

TRACING LINES

 Trace.

 -

 -

 -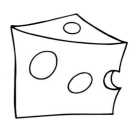

 -

 Trace.

Trace.

Name _____

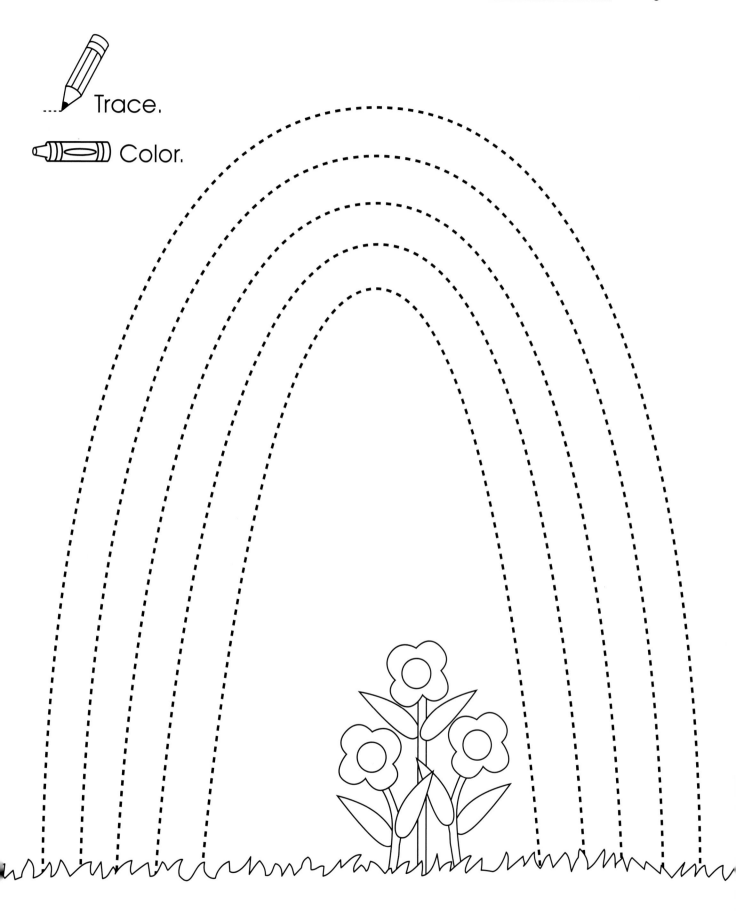

Trace.

Color.

Trace.

Color.

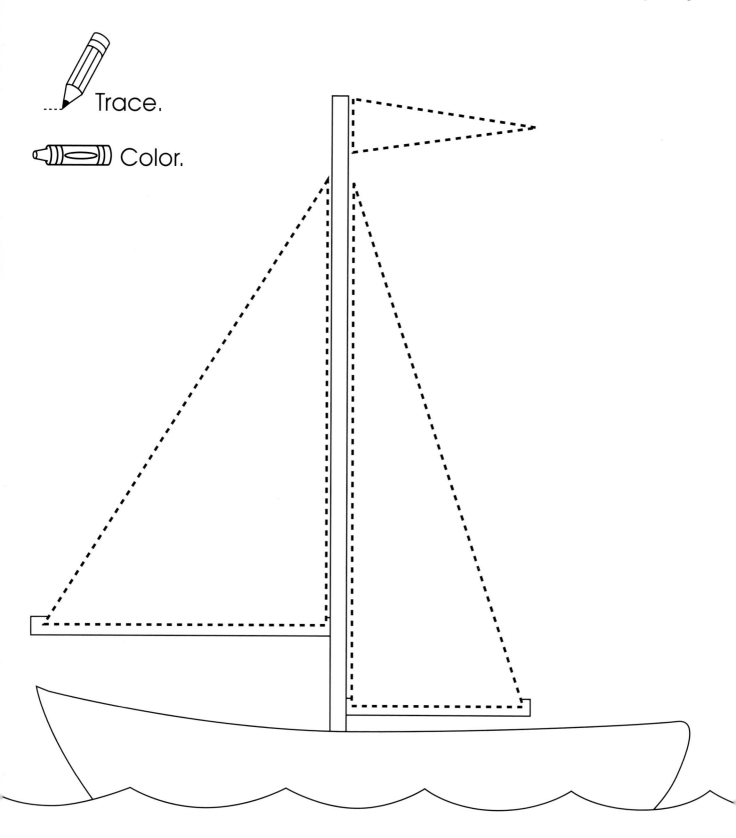

Name _____ *Tracing: squares*

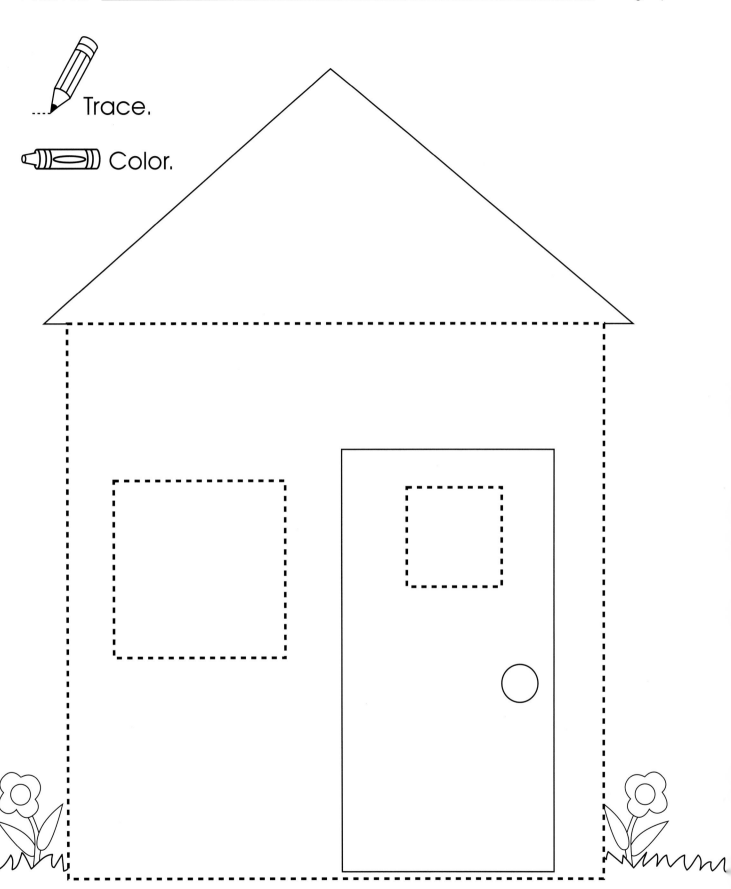

Trace.

Color.

Name _____

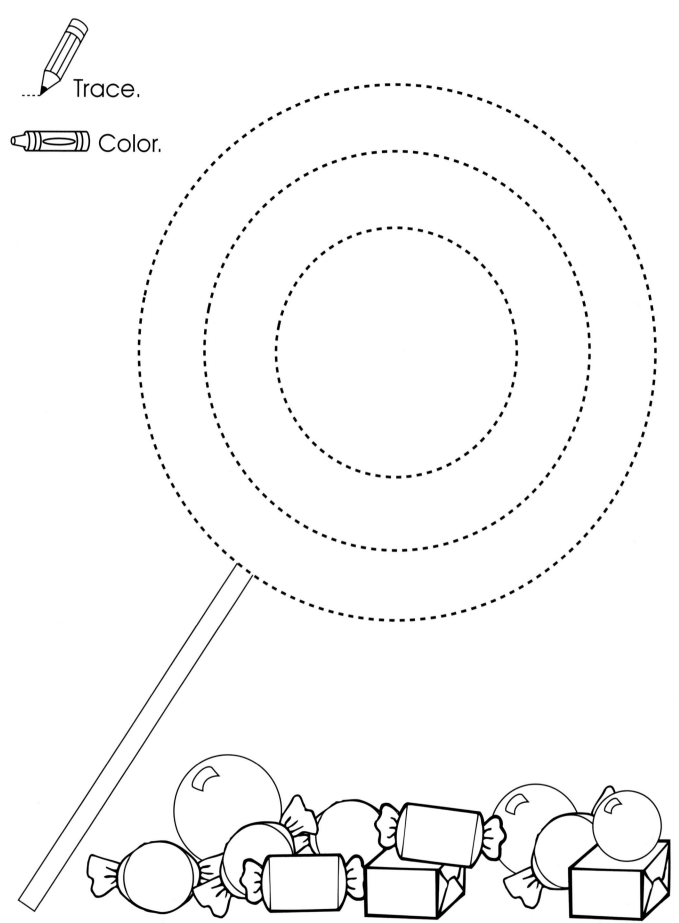

✏️ Trace.

🖍️ Color.

PART TWO

CUT & PASTE ACTIVITIES

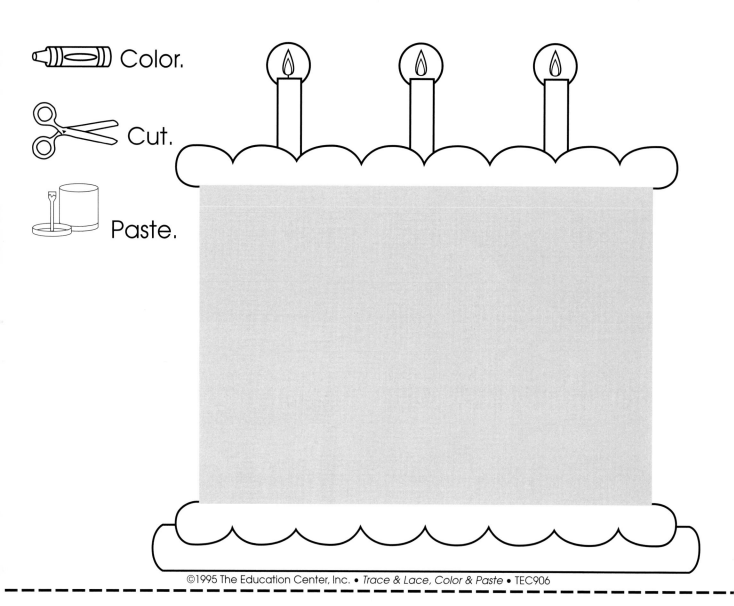

Color.

Cut.

Paste.

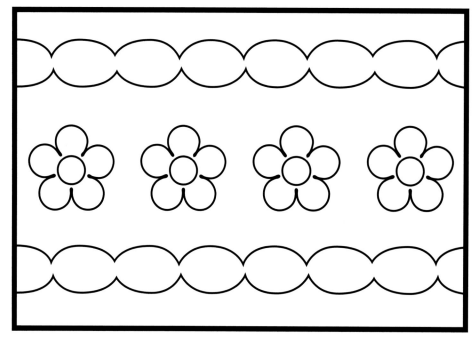

 Color.

 Cut.

Paste.

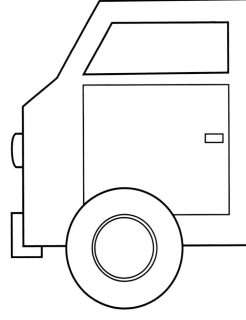

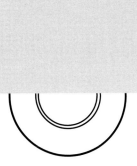

©1995 The Education Center, Inc. • *Trace & Lace, Color & Paste* • TEC906

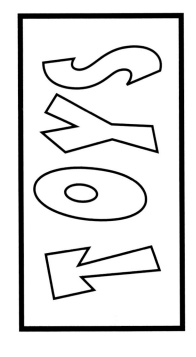

 Color.

 Cut.

Paste.

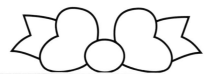

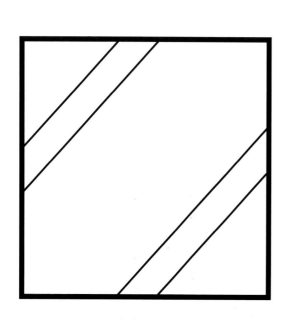

14

 Color.

 Cut.

Paste.

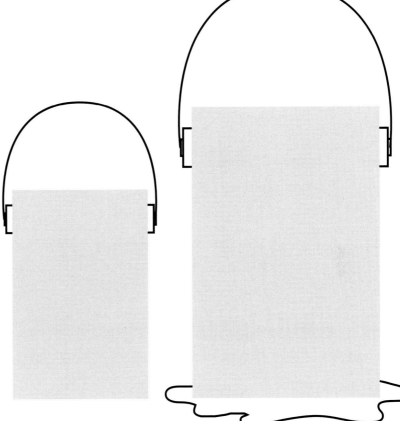

- -

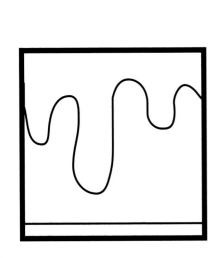

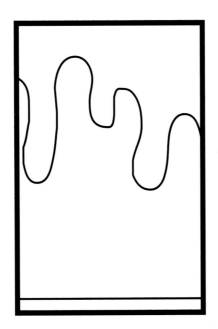

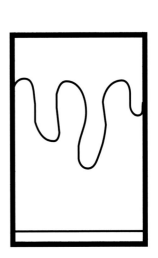

 Color.

 Cut.

Paste.

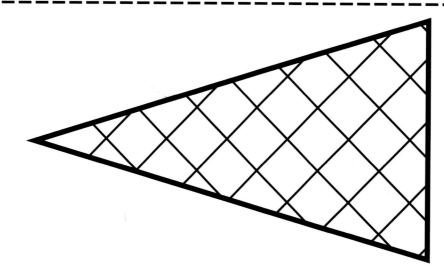

Name _____

Color.

Cut.

Paste.

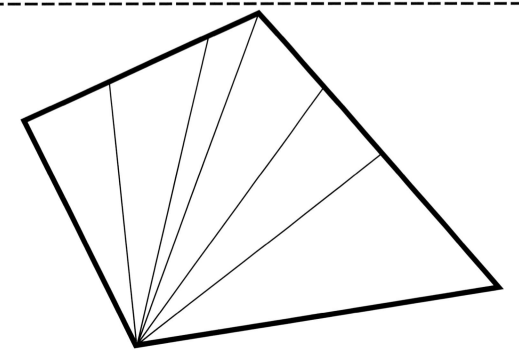

 Color.

 Cut.

 Paste.

©1995 The Education Center, Inc. • *Trace & Lace, Color & Paste* • TEC906

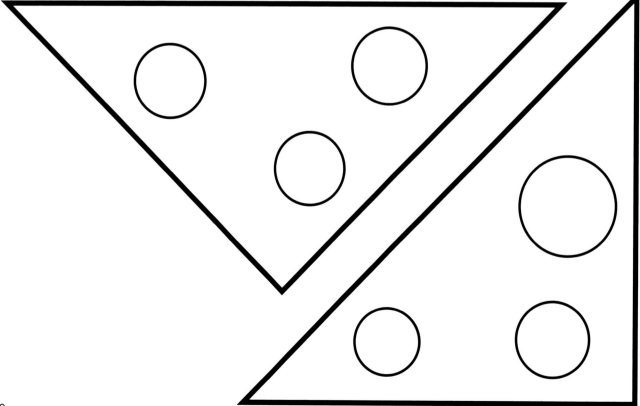

18

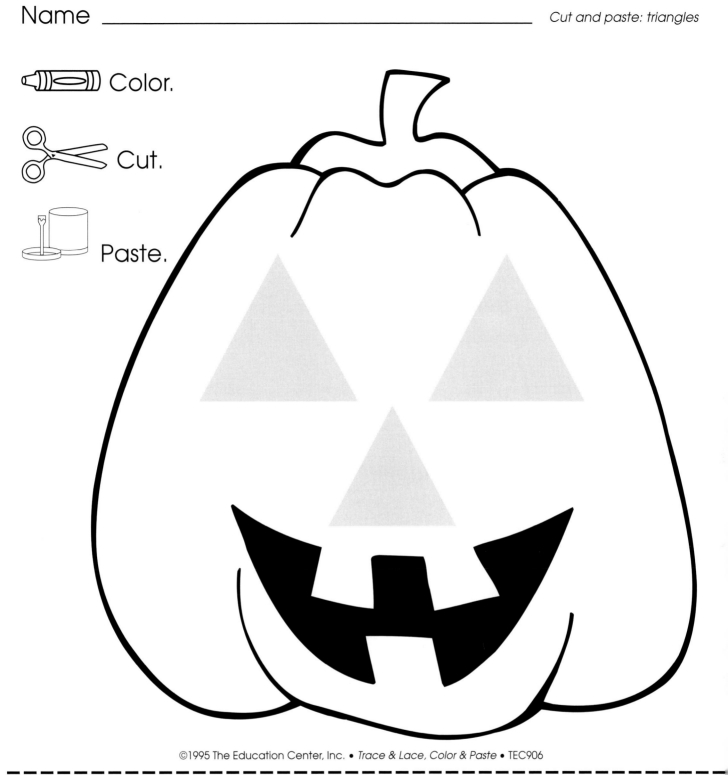

Color.

Cut.

Paste.

©1995 The Education Center, Inc. • *Trace & Lace, Color & Paste* • TEC906

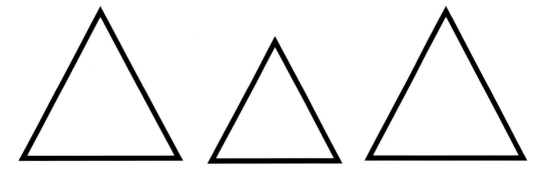

Color.

Cut.

Paste.

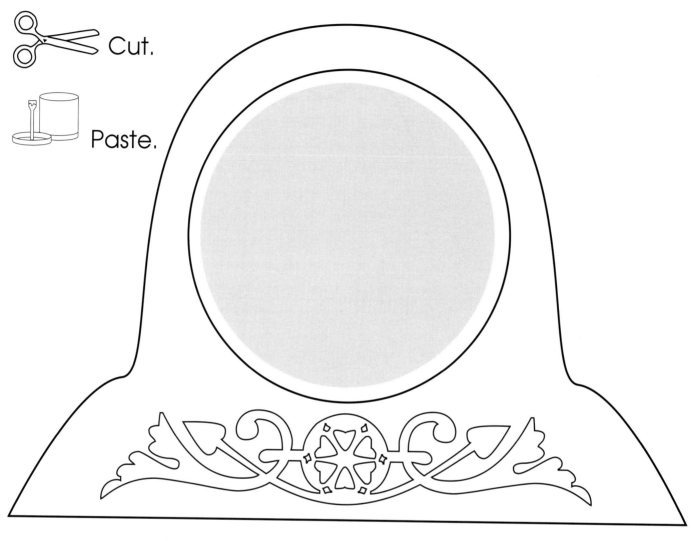

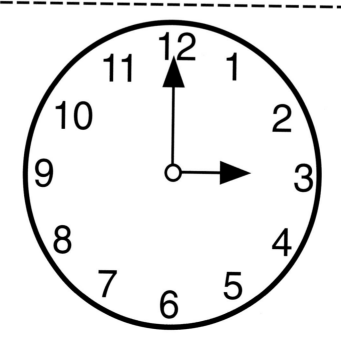

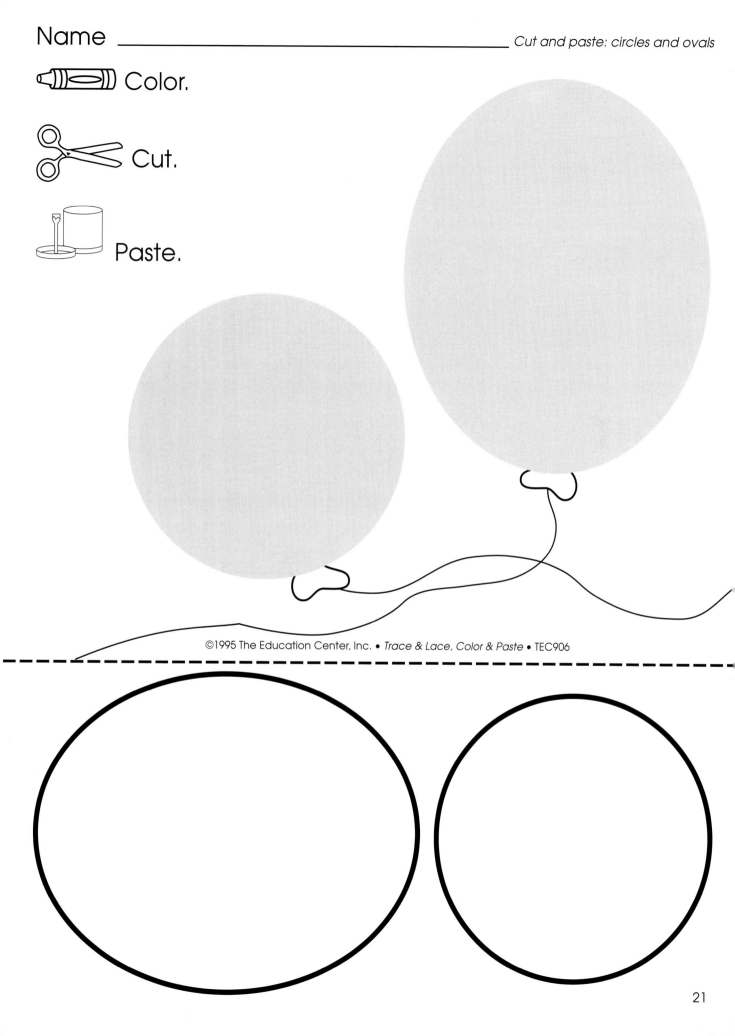

Color.

Cut.

Paste.

©1995 The Education Center, Inc. • *Trace & Lace, Color & Paste* • TEC906

21

Color.

Cut.

Paste.

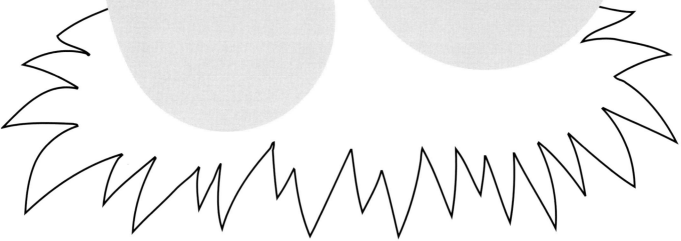

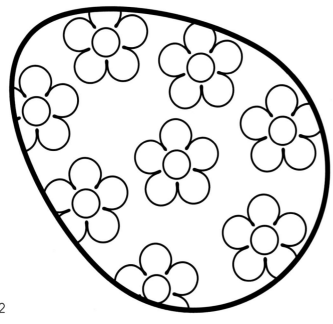

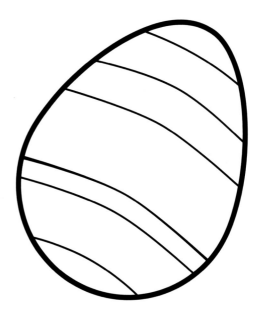

Name _____

 Color.

 Cut.

Paste.

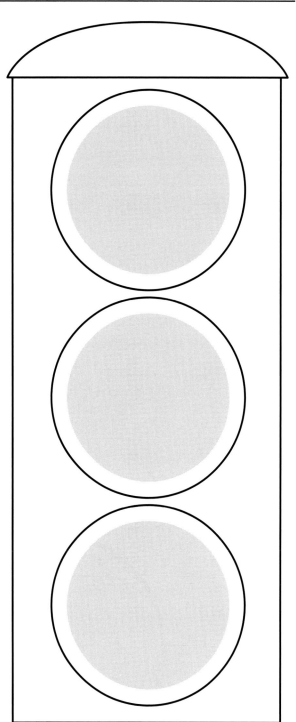

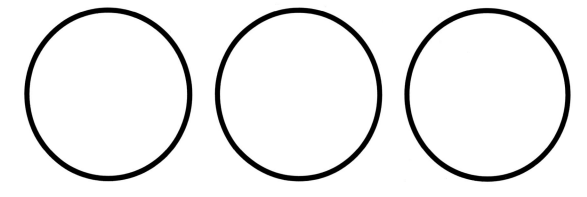

23

Cut and paste: combination of shapes

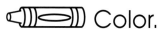 Color.

 Cut.

 Paste.

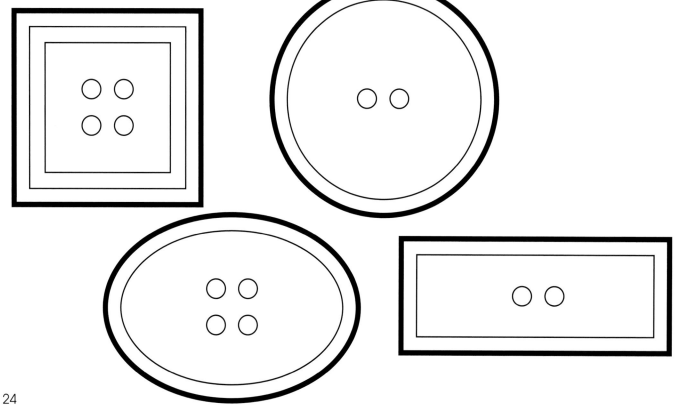

Color.

Cut.

Paste.

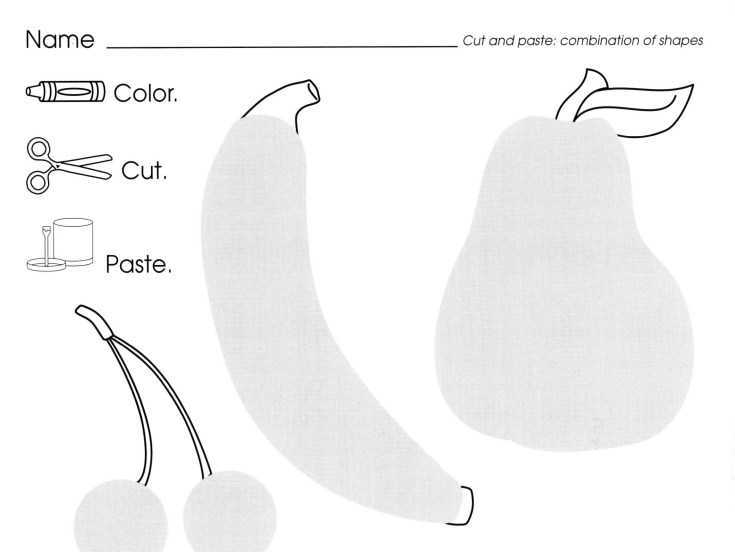

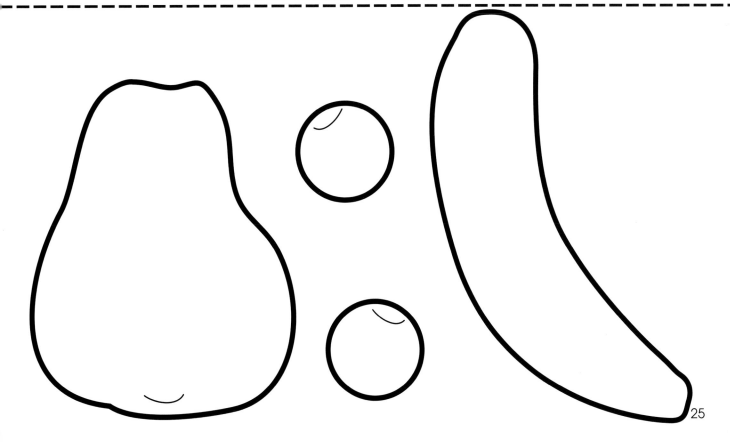

25

 Color.

 Cut.

Paste.

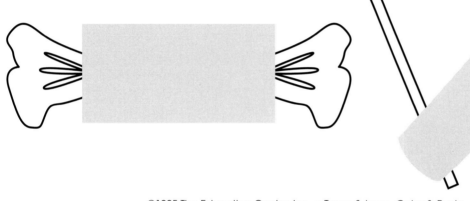

©1995 The Education Center, Inc. • *Trace & Lace, Color & Paste* • TEC906

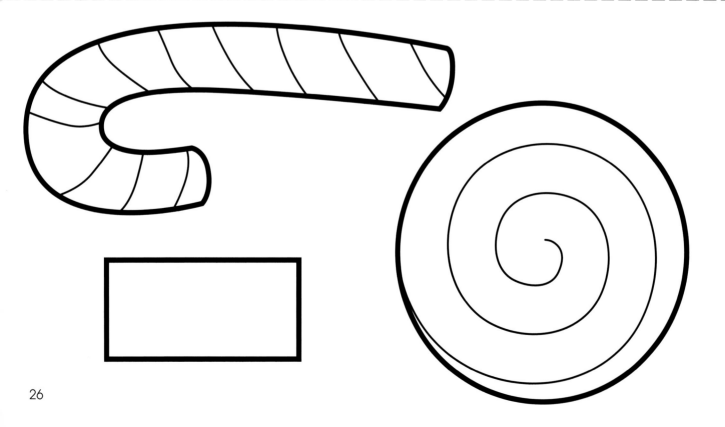

Name _____ *Cut and paste: combination of shapes*

 Color.

 Cut.

Paste.

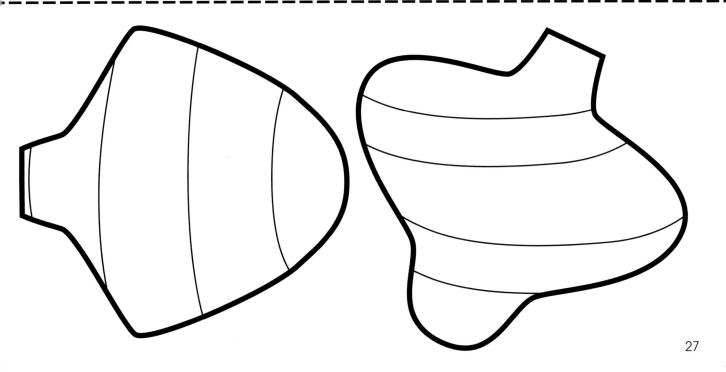

27

Cut and paste: combination of shapes

 Color.

 Cut.

 Paste.

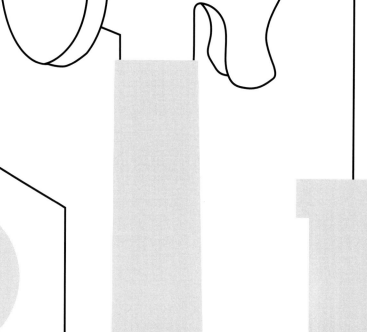

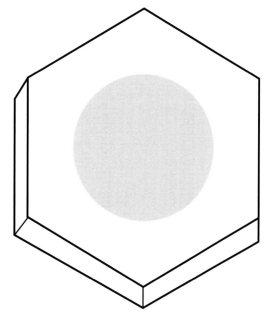

©1995 The Education Center, Inc. • *Trace & Lace, Color & Paste* • TEC906

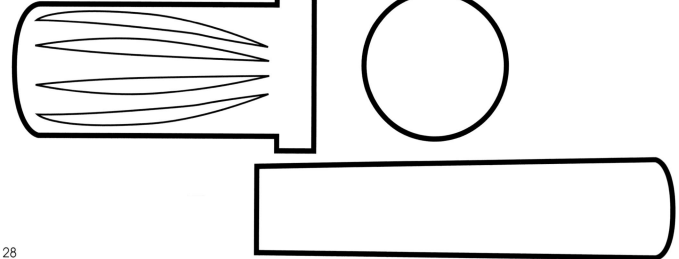

28

Cut and paste: combination of shapes

Color.

Cut.

Paste.

Cut and paste: combination of shapes

 Color.

 Cut.

 Paste.

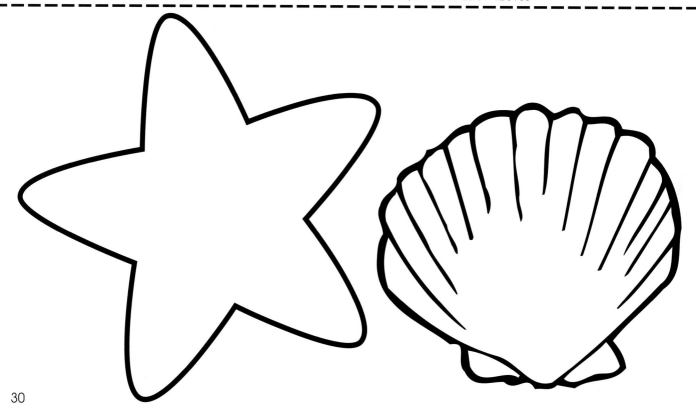

PART THREE

PATTERN PROJECTS

APPLE AND WORM

Skills:
trace
cut
finger-paint
glue
tear
draw

Materials:

apple and leaf patterns
tagboard
1 sheet white finger-paint paper
red finger paint
green finger paint
1 sheet blue construction paper

black construction-paper scrap
1/4 sheet brown construction paper
scissors
glue
marker
crayon or pencil

To prepare, duplicate the apple and leaf patterns on several sheets of tagboard. Cut them out for children to use as templates.

Directions:

1. Trace the apple and leaf patterns on white finger-paint paper. Cut them out.
2. Finger-paint the apple with red paint and the leaf with green paint. Allow them to dry.
3. Glue the apple to the center of the blue construction paper.
4. Tear a stem from brown construction paper and glue it at the top of the apple.
5. Glue on the leaf.
6. Tear a hole from black construction paper and glue it on the apple.
7. Tear a worm from brown construction paper and glue it on the hole.
8. Use a marker to draw two eyes on the worm.

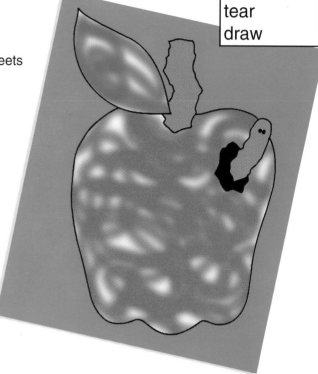

TRAVELIN' TURTLE

Skills:
tear
cut
glue
draw

Materials:

turtle head, feet, and tail patterns
unprinted side of a brown paper grocery bag
1 sheet of green construction paper
scissors
glue
marker

To prepare, duplicate the turtle head, feet, and tail patterns on green construction paper for each child.

Directions:

1. Tear an oval shape from a piece of brown grocery bag.
2. Cut out the head, feet, and tail patterns.
3. Tear the green paper scraps into pieces and glue onto the brown oval to decorate the turtle's shell.
4. Glue the head, feet, and tail to the underside of the oval as shown.
5. Use a marker to draw eyes and toes.

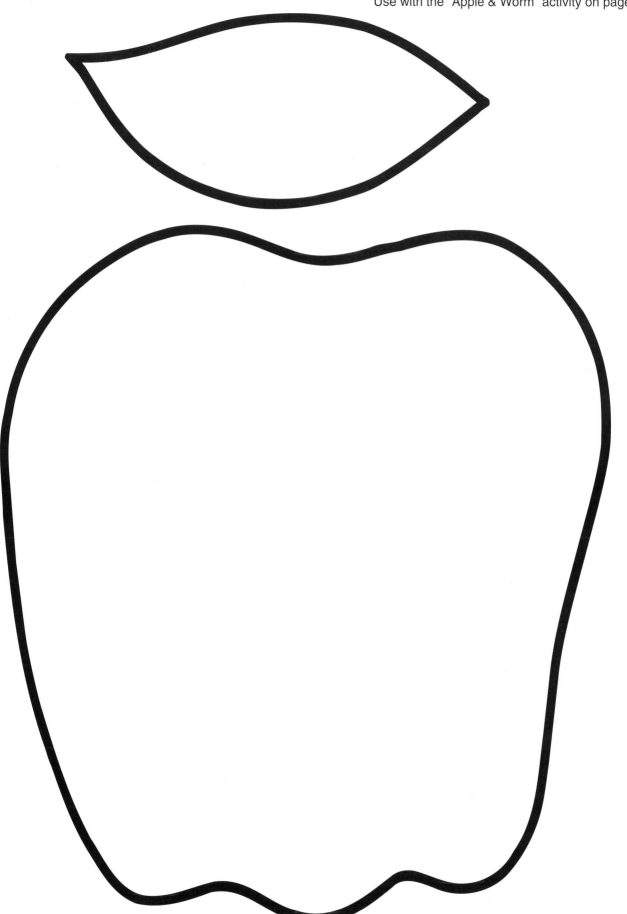

Patterns

Use with the "Travelin' Turtle" activity on page 32.

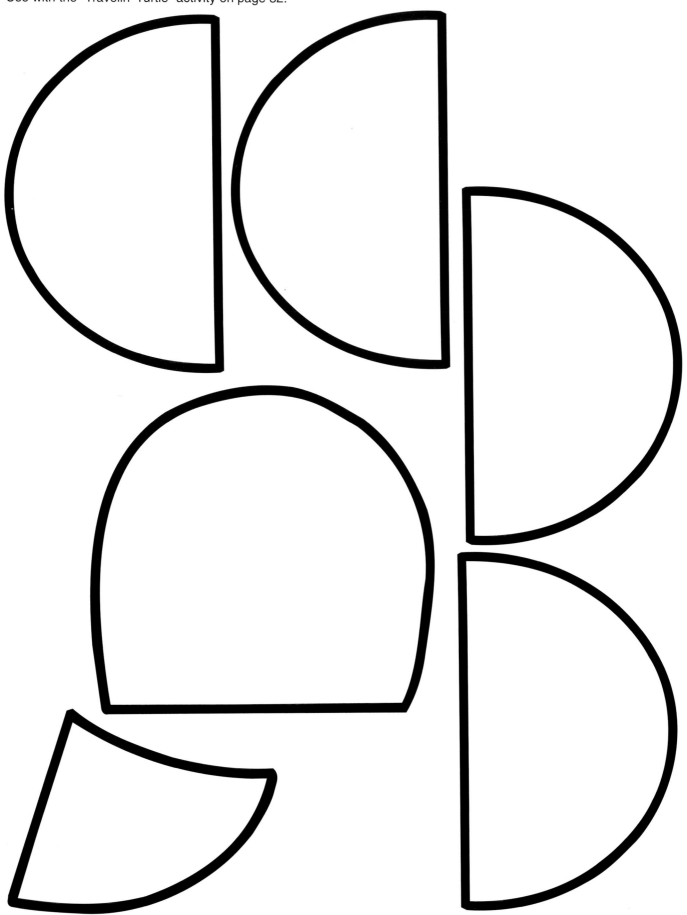

DALMATIAN EARS

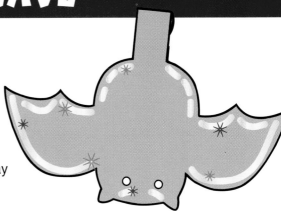

Skills:
trace
cut
glue
hole-punch

Materials:
Dalmatian ear pattern
tagboard
sheets white construction paper
sheet black construction paper
scissors
glue
plastic headband
hole puncher
crayon or pencil

To prepare, duplicate the Dalmatian ear pattern on several sheets of tagboard. Cut the copies out for children to use as templates.

Directions:
1. Trace the ear pattern on two sheets of white construction paper. Cut them
2. Glue the ears together as shown.
3. Cut out several spots from black construction paper.
4. Glue the spots on the ears.
5. Use a hole puncher to make two holes, six inches apart, in the center.
6. Push a plastic headband through the two holes.

Glue here.

BAT CAVE

Skills:
cut
hole-punch
fold
glue

Materials:
bat pattern
1 sheet gray construction paper
scissors
hole puncher
glue
glitter glue

To prepare, duplicate the bat pattern on gray construction paper for each child.

Directions:
1. Cut out the bat pattern.
2. Use a hole puncher to make two eyes.
3. Fold on the dotted line and glue to make a loop for hanging.
4. Use a tube of glitter glue to add sparkle to the bat. Allow the glue to dry.
5. Suspend the bats upside down from the classroom ceiling to create a bat cave.

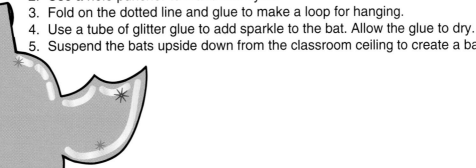

Pattern

Use with the "Dalmatian Ears" activity on page 35.

OWL PUPPET

Skills:
cut
glue
draw
fold

Materials:
owl head, eyes, eyebrows, and beak patterns
1 sheet brown construction paper
1/2 sheet orange construction paper
1/2 sheet yellow construction paper
1/2 sheet gray construction paper
jumbo craft stick
scissors
glue
marker

To prepare, duplicate the head pattern on brown construction paper, the beak pattern on orange construction paper, the eyes on yellow construction paper, and the eyebrows on gray construction paper for each child.

Directions:
1. Cut out the head, eyes, eyebrows, and beak patterns.
2. Glue a jumbo craft stick to the back of the head as shown.
3. Glue the eyes on the front of the head.
4. Glue the eyebrows above the eyes.
5. Use a marker to draw a pupil in the center of each eye.
6. Fold the orange pattern to make a beak and glue to the owl as shown.

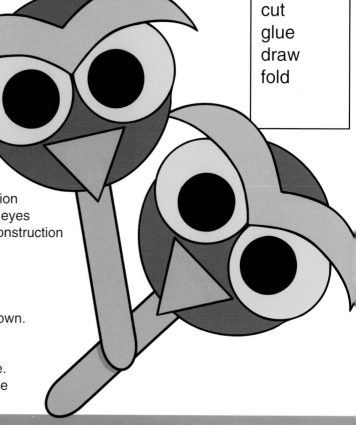

INDIAN CORN

Skills:
cut
glue
crumple

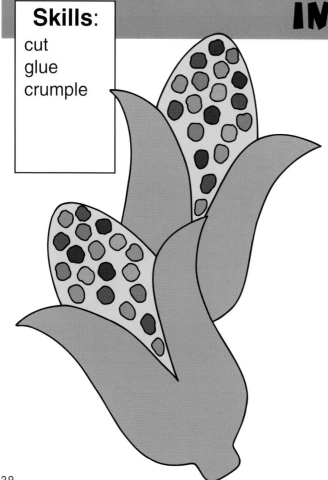

Materials:
husk and corn cob patterns
1/2 sheet yellow construction paper
1/2 sheet brown construction paper
2" x 2" colored tissue-paper squares
scissors
glue

To prepare, duplicate the husk pattern on brown construction paper and the corn cob pattern on yellow construction paper for each child.

Directions:
1. Cut out the husk and corn cob patterns.
2. Glue the corn cob to the husk as shown.
3. Crumple several squares of colored tissue paper into balls.
4. Glue the tissue-paper balls to the corn cob.

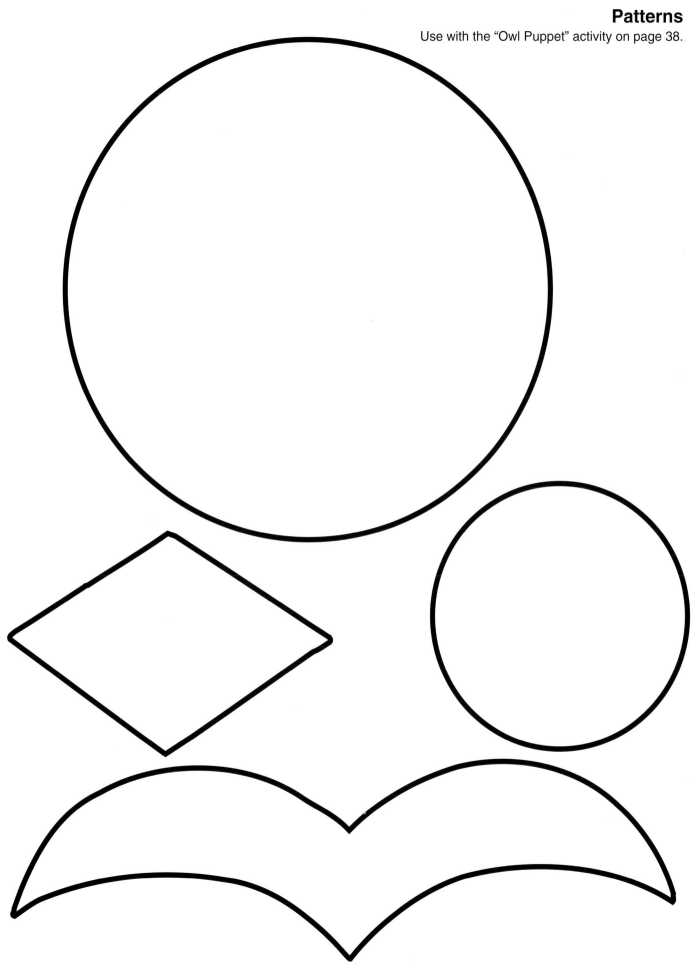

Patterns

Use with the "Indian Corn" activity on page 38.

CHRISTMAS TREE

Materials:

Christmas tree pattern

1 sheet green construction paper

1 1/2" cardboard tube

colored circular stickers

scissors

To prepare, duplicate the Christmas tree pattern on green construction paper for each child. Cut two vertical slits in the top of each cardboard tube.

Directions:

1. Cut out the Christmas tree pattern.
2. Attach several colored circular stickers to the front and back of the tree.
3. Slide the base of the tree into the two slits cut in the cardboard tube.

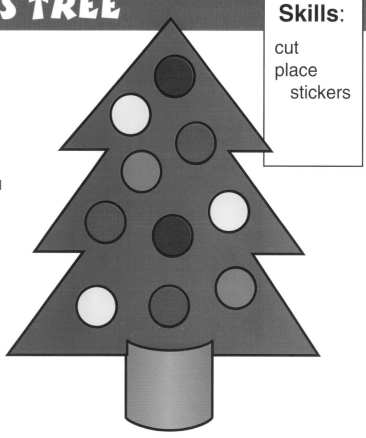

GINGERBREAD BOY

Skills:

cut

place

stickers

draw

glue

Materials:

gingerbread boy pattern

1 sheet brown construction paper

2 circular stickers

rickrack

buttons

scissors

glue

marker

To prepare, duplicate the gingerbread boy pattern on brown construction paper for each child.

Directions:

1. Cut out the gingerbread boy pattern.
2. Stick the circular stickers on the face to make cheeks.
3. Use a marker to draw the eyes and mouth.
4. Glue buttons and rickrack on the gingerbread boy as shown. Allow the glue to dry.

Pattern

Use with the "Christmas Tree" activity on page 41.

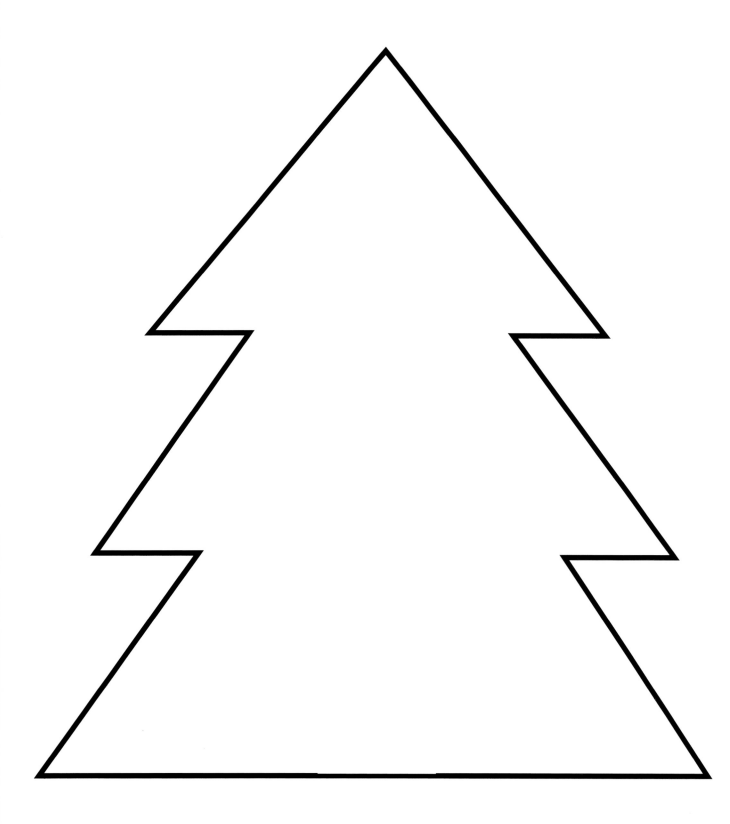

FROSTY SNOWMAN

Materials:

snowman pattern
tagboard
1 sheet white construction paper
colored construction-paper scraps
light blue tempera paint
12" x 12" square of thick cardboard

pushpins
scissors
sponge piece
glue
marker

To prepare, duplicate the snowman pattern on several sheets of tagboard. Cut them out for children to use as templates. Attach each child's sheet of white paper to the cardboard using pushpins. Attach a snowman template on top of the white paper with pushpins.

Directions:
1. Sponge-paint light blue tempera paint on the white paper around the snowman pattern.
2. When the paint is dry, have the teacher remove the snowman pattern and remove the painted paper from the cardboard.
3. Use a marker to draw the eyes.
4. Tear construction-paper scraps to create the nose, arms, scarf, and buttons. Glue the pieces on the snowman as shown.

VALENTINE PUZZLE

Materials:

valentine puzzle piece patterns
1 sheet white construction paper
1/2 sheet red construction paper
1/2 sheet pink construction paper
1/2 sheet purple construction paper
scissors
glue

To prepare, duplicate each of the puzzle piece pattern pieces on a different color of construction paper (use red, pink, and purple) for each child.

Directions:
1. Cut out each puzzle piece.
2. Assemble the puzzle pieces on white paper as shown.
3. Glue the puzzle pieces to the white paper.

PARTY MASK

Materials:

mask pattern
tagboard
colored circular stickers
small paper dollies
colored feathers

3 strands colored ribbon
jumbo craft stick
masking tape
scissors
glue

To prepare, duplicate the mask pattern on a sheet of tagboard for each child. Cut out each mask and the two holes for the eyes.

Directions:

1. Use circular stickers to decorate the mask.
2. Glue three paper doilies on the mask as shown.
3. Glue three feathers on the mask as shown.
4. Tape three strands of ribbon on the left underside of the mask.
5. Tape a jumbo craft stick to the right underside of the mask.

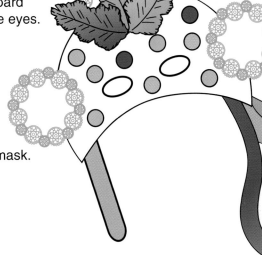

SLIPPERY SNAKE

Skills:

sponge-
   paint
cut
glue
draw
tear

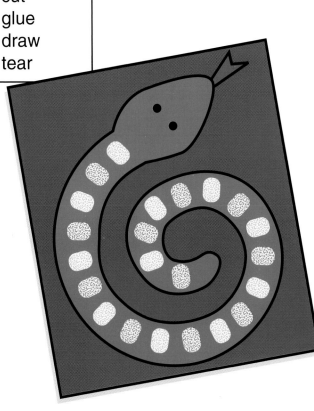

Materials:

snake pattern
1 sheet green construction paper
1 sheet purple construction paper
1 red construction-paper scrap
yellow tempera paint
orange tempera paint
2 sponge pieces
scissors
glue
marker

To prepare, duplicate the snake pattern on green construction paper for each child.

Directions:

1. Sponge-paint the snake with yellow and orange tempera paint. Allow the paint to dry.
2. Cut out the snake pattern and glue it to the purple paper.
3. Use a marker to draw the snake's eyes.
4. Tear a tongue from the red construction-paper scrap and glue on as shown.

Pattern
Use with the "Party Mask" activity on page 47.

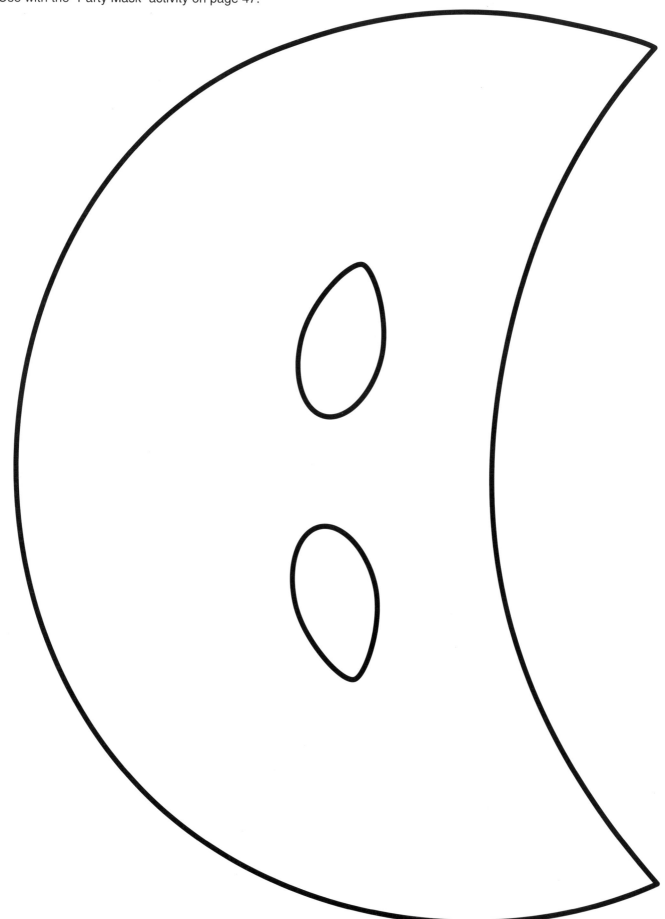

HUMPTY DUMPTY

Materials:

egg pattern
tagboard
1 sheet 12" x 18" yellow construction paper
1 sheet green construction paper
1 sheet purple construction paper

colored construction-paper scraps
scissors
glue
marker
crayon or pencil

To prepare, duplicate the egg pattern on several sheets of tagboard. Cut the copies out for children to use as templates.

Directions:

1. Use a marker to draw a brick wall on yellow construction paper as shown.
2. Trace the egg pattern on green construction paper. Cut it out.
3. Glue the egg on the yellow paper as shown.
4. Tear the eyes, nose, and mouth from construction-paper scraps and glue on the egg.
5. Tear the arms and legs from purple construction paper and glue on the egg.

JOLLY CLOWN PUPPET

Materials:

clown body, head, and hat patterns
1 sheet yellow construction paper
1/4 sheet purple construction paper
two 1" x 6" red construction-paper strips
two 1" x 9" red construction-paper strips
2 circular stickers
rickrack

buttons
plastic drinking straw
paper cutter
tape
scissors
glue
marker

To prepare, duplicate the clown body and head patterns on yellow construction paper and the hat pattern on purple construction paper for each child. Use a paper cutter to cut strips from red construction paper.

Directions:

1. Cut out the clown's body, head, and hat.
2. Glue the hat to the head. Glue the head to the body.
3. Stick two circular stickers to the face to make cheeks.
4. Glue on two small buttons for eyes.
5. Use a marker to draw the mouth.
6. Decorate the body with buttons and rickrack as shown.
7. Accordion-fold the two 1" x 6" strips of red construction paper to make the arms and the two 1" x 9" strips to make the legs.
8. Glue the arms and legs to the underside of the body as shown.
9. Tape a plastic drinking straw to the back of the body for a handle.

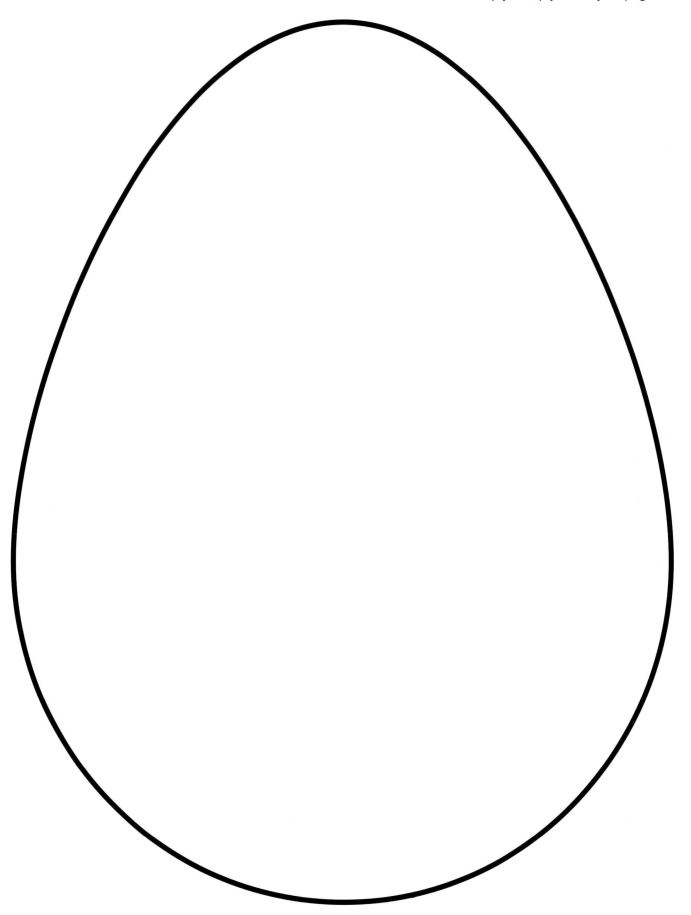

Patterns

Use with the "Jolly Clown Puppet" activity on page 50.

DUTCH WINDMILL

Materials:

windmill and blade patterns
1 sheet 12" x 18" light blue construction paper
1 sheet orange construction paper
1 sheet yellow construction paper
green tempera paint
yellow tempera paint
red tempera paint

white tempera paint
brad
scissors
glue
fork
pencils
cotton ball

To prepare, duplicate the windmill pattern on orange construction paper and the blade pattern on yellow construction paper for each child.

Directions:

1. Cut out the windmill and blade patterns.
2. Glue the windmill on light blue construction paper as shown.
3. Attach the blades to the windmill with a brad.
4. To make the grass, use a fork to print green paint on the blue paper as shown.
5. Use the eraser end of a pencil dipped in tempera paint to print yellow and red flowers above the grass.
6. Use a cotton ball to print white clouds on the blue paper as shown.

EASTER EGG

Materials:

egg pattern
tagboard
1 sheet yellow construction paper
1 sheet purple construction paper
sequins
ribbon
scissors
glue
crayon or pencil

To prepare, duplicate the egg pattern on several sheets of tagboard. Cut the copies out for children to use as templates.

Directions:

1. Trace the egg pattern on yellow construction paper. Cut it out.
2. Cut the egg into three parts horizontally.
3. Put the egg together again on purple construction paper, leaving a little space between each piece.
4. Once the egg is in place, glue it to the purple paper.
5. Glue sequins on the egg and ribbon in the space between the three pieces.

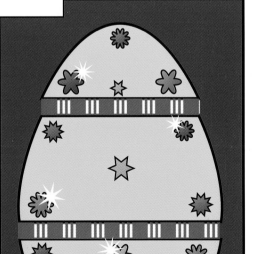

Pattern
Use with the "Dutch Windmill" activity on page 53.

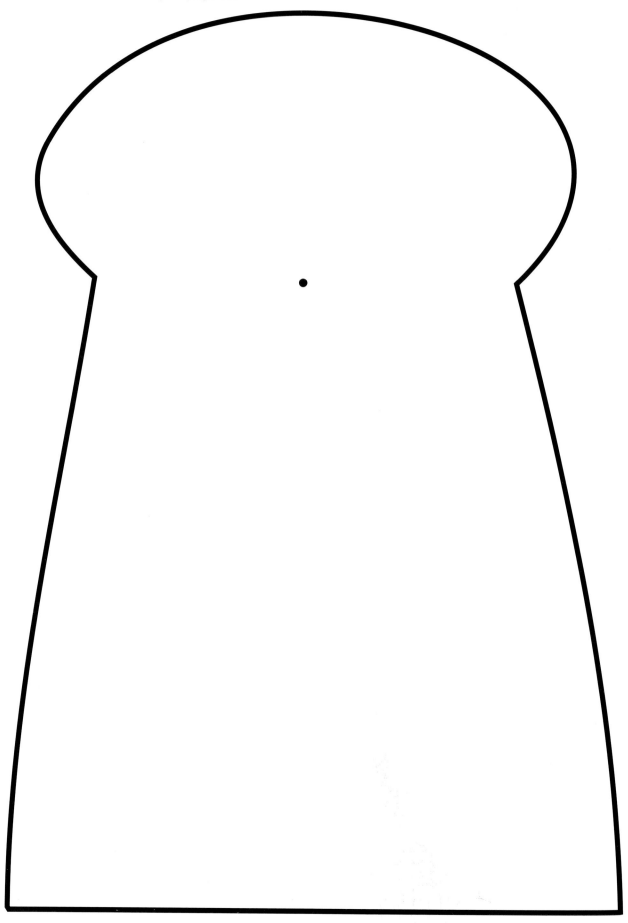

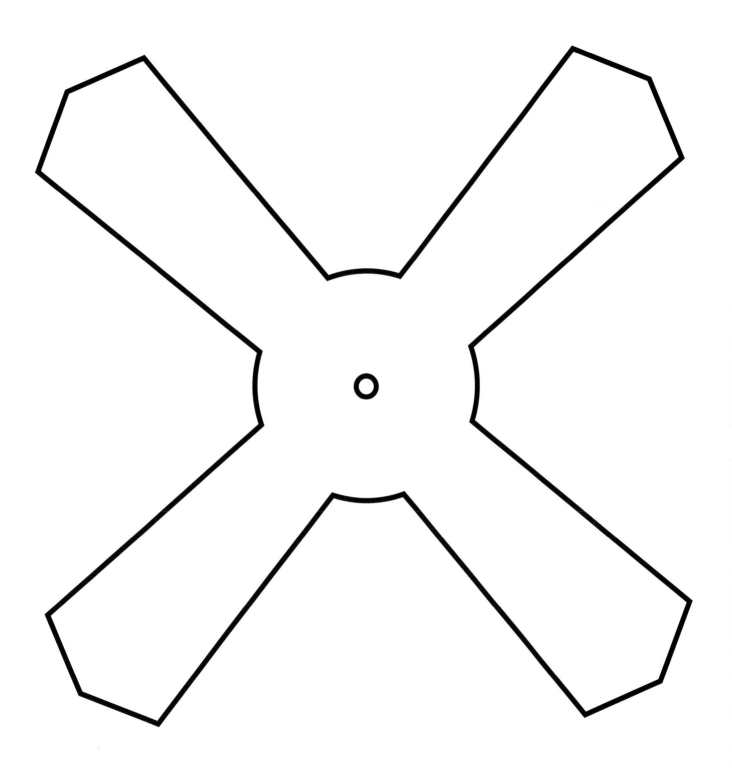

Pattern

Use with the "Easter Egg" activity on page 53.

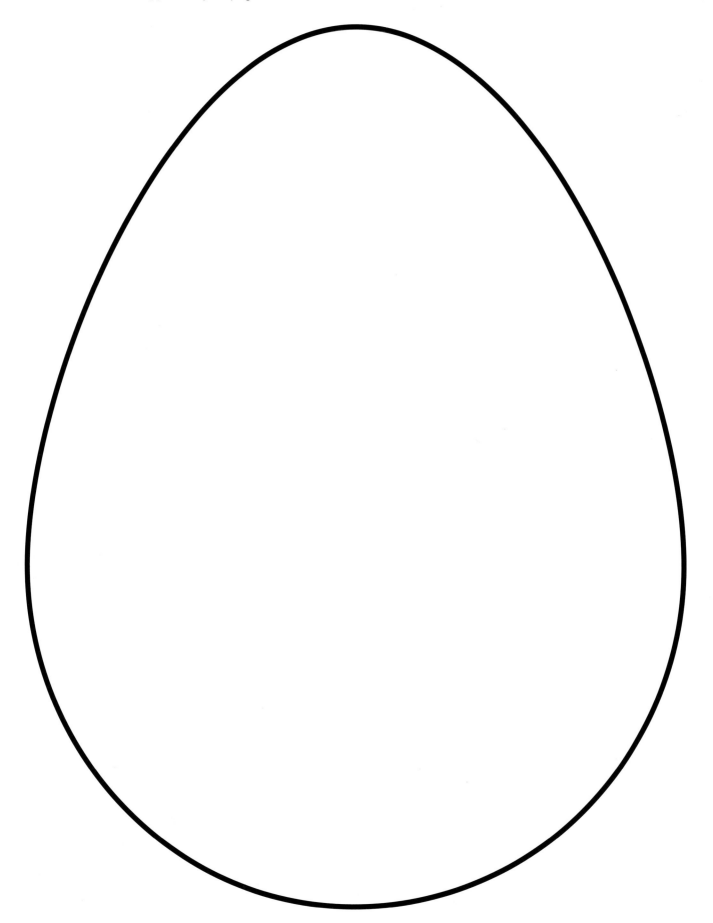

MARY'S LITTLE LAMB

Materials:
lamb head, face, ear, tongue, and nose patterns
1 sheet white construction paper
1 sheet gray construction paper
1/2 sheet pink construction paper
cotton balls
scissors
glue

To prepare, duplicate the head pattern on white construction paper, the face and ear patterns on gray construction paper, and the tongue and nose patterns on pink construction paper for each child.

Directions:
1. Cut out the head, face, ear, tongue, and nose patterns.
2. Glue the face and the ears on the underside of the head as shown.
3. Glue the tongue on the underside of the face.
4. Glue the nose on the face.
5. Glue cotton balls on the head as shown.

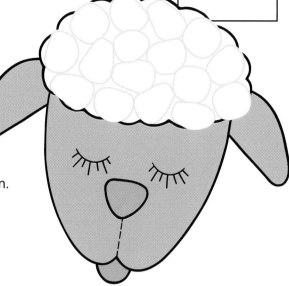

MAY FLOWER

Materials:
leaves/flower pattern
1 sheet green construction paper
1 sheet brightly colored construction paper
2" x 2" colored tissue-paper squares
scissors
glue

To prepare, duplicate the leaves/flower pattern once on green and once on brightly colored construction paper for each child.

Directions:
1. Cut out the two patterns.
2. Glue the colored flower to the green leaves as shown.
3. Crumple several 2" x 2" tissue-paper squares into balls.
4. Glue the balls onto the center of the flower. Allow the glue to dry.

57

Patterns

Use with the "Mary's Little Lamb" activity on page 57.

DEEP-SEA FISH

Skills:

print
trace
cut
sponge-
    paint
glue
tear

Materials:

fish pattern
tagboard
1 sheet white construction paper
1 sheet blue construction paper
1 sheet orange construction paper
1 black construction-paper scrap
white tempera paint

yellow tempera paint
red tempera paint
cardboard tube
2 sponge pieces
scissors
glue
crayon or pencil

To prepare, duplicate the fish pattern on several sheets of tagboard. Cut the copies out for children to use as templates.

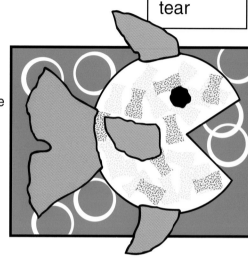

Directions:

1. Dip one end of the cardboard tube in white tempera paint. Use the tube to print white circles on blue construction paper. Allow the paint to dry.
2. Trace the fish pattern on white construction paper. Cut out the pattern.
3. Sponge-paint the fish with yellow and red tempera paint. Allow the paint to dry.
4. Glue the fish to the blue construction paper as shown.
5. Tear a tail and three fins from orange construction paper and glue them to the fish.
6. Tear an eye from the black construction-paper scrap and glue it to the fish.

WATERMELON SLICE

Skills:

sponge-
    paint
trace
cut
glue
print

Materials:

watermelon slice patterns
tagboard
1 sheet white paper
1 sheet red construction paper
1 sheet green construction paper
red tempera paint
black tempera paint
square sponge
scissors
glue
cotton swab
crayon or pencil

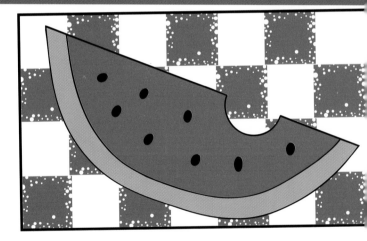

To prepare, duplicate the watermelon slice patterns on several sheets of tagboard. Cut the copies out for children to use as templates.

Directions:

1. Sponge-paint red tempera paint on a sheet of white paper to create a checkerboard pattern. Allow the paint to dry.
2. Trace the small watermelon slice pattern on red construction paper. Cut it out.
3. Trace the large watermelon slice pattern on green construction paper. Cut it out.
4. Glue the small piece on the large piece as shown.
5. Glue the watermelon slice on the checkerboard background.
6. Dip a cotton swab in black tempera paint. Use the cotton swab to print seeds on the watermelon.

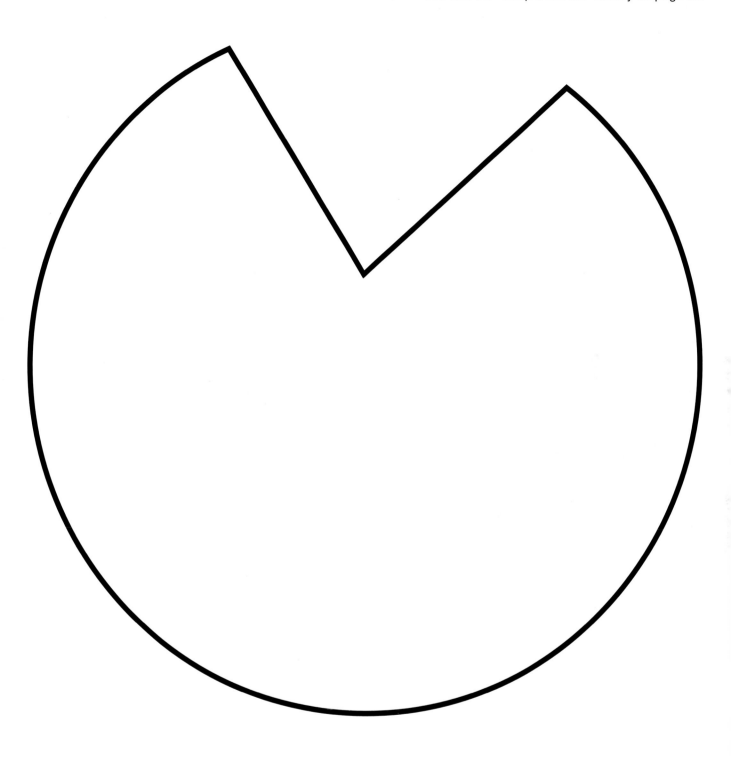

Patterns

Use with the "Watermelon Slice" activity on page 60.

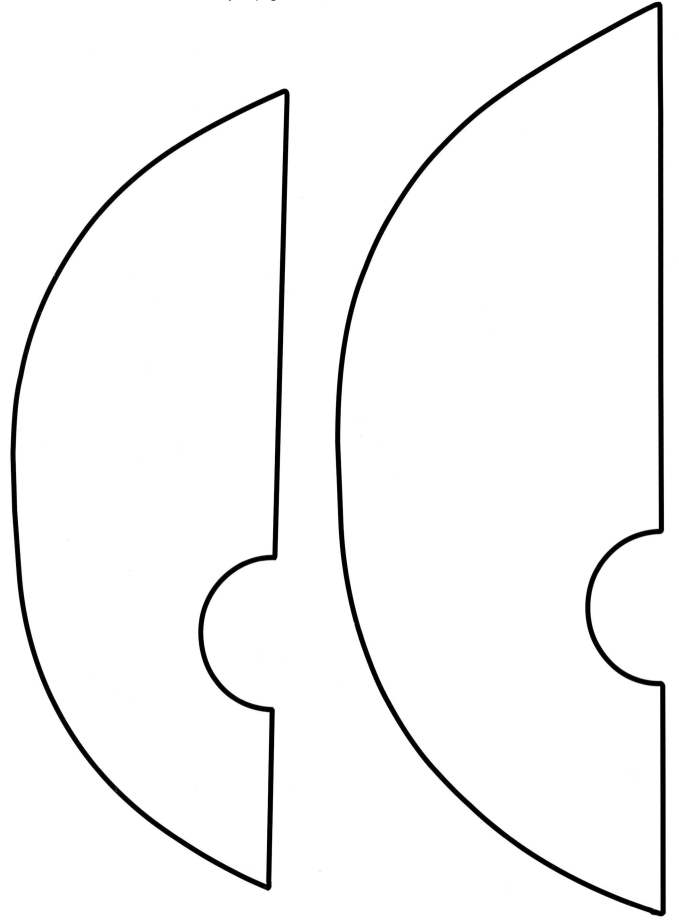

TROPICAL OCTOPUS

Materials:

octopus head and legs patterns
1 sheet 12" x 18" blue construction paper
2 sheets pink construction paper
1 sheet green construction paper
colored construction-paper scraps
white tempera paint

red tempera paint
scissors
glue
plastic spool
pencil

To prepare, duplicate the octopus head and legs patterns on pink construction paper for each child.

Directions:

1. Use a plastic spool to print white paint on the octopus head and legs patterns.
2. Use the eraser end of a pencil to print red dots on the patterns.
3. Allow the paint to dry.
4. Cut out the head and legs patterns and glue to the blue construction paper as shown.
5. Tear the eyes, nose, and mouth from construction-paper scraps. Glue to the head.
6. Tear seaweed from green construction paper. Glue to the blue paper as shown.

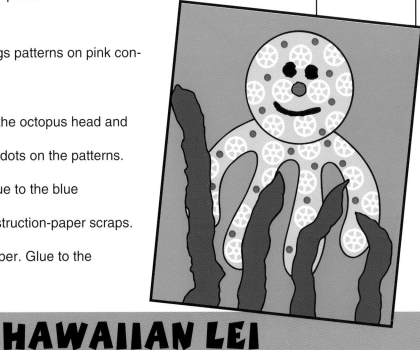

HAWAIIAN LEI

Skills:

cut
place
stickers
hole-punch
lace

Materials:

flower and leaf patterns
1/2 sheet orange construction paper
1/2 sheet red construction paper
1/2 sheet yellow construction paper
1 sheet green construction paper
3 circular stickers
36" length of yarn
scissors
hole puncher

To prepare, duplicate enough copies of the flower pattern so that each child has one orange, one yellow, and one red flower. Duplicate four copies of the leaf pattern on green construction paper for each child.

Directions:

1. Cut out the flower and leaf patterns.
2. Stick a circular sticker to the center of each flower.
3. Use a hole puncher to make two holes in each flower and one in each leaf as shown.
4. Lace a strand of yarn through the holes as shown and tie the ends together.

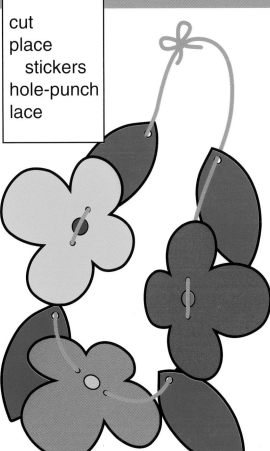

63

Pattern

Use with the "Tropical Octopus" activity on page 63.

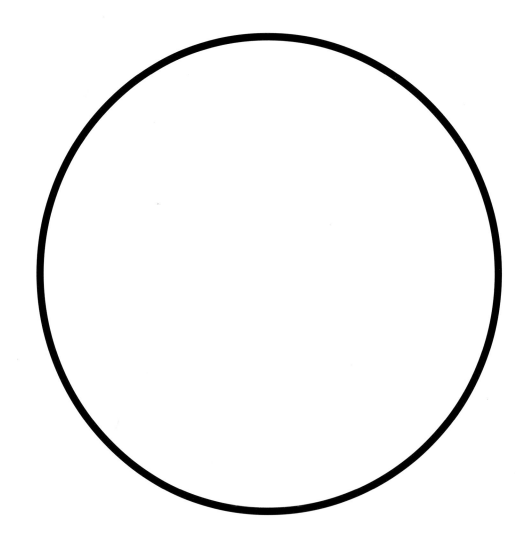

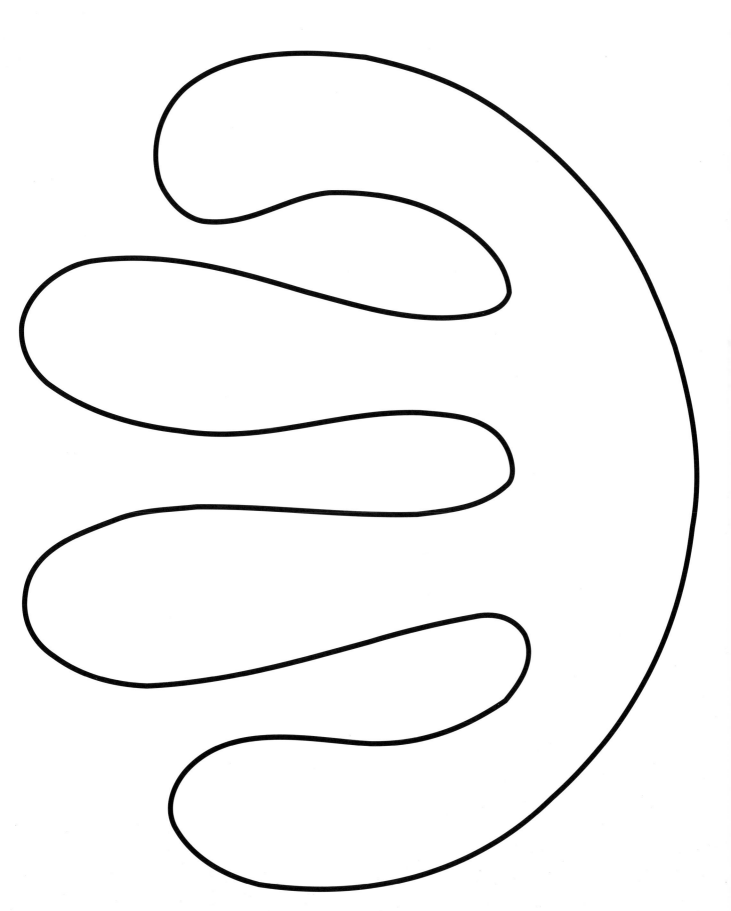

Pattern

Use with the "Hawaiian Lei" activity on page 63.

PART FOUR

FINE-MOTOR ACTIVITIES

COOKING CAPERS

Banana Split Sundae

Cool off on a hot day with this delicious treat! Give each child a plastic knife and one-half of a banana. Tell him to use the knife to slice the banana. Place the slices in a bowl. Spoon thawed whipped topping over the banana slices. Decorate with candy sprinkles and a cherry.

Pinwheel Roll-Ups

Your youngsters will enjoy making and eating this yummy snack. Give each child in a small group one slice of bread. Let her use a plastic knife to trim the crust from the bread. Roll the bread flat with a rolling pin. Use the knife to spread a thin layer of peanut butter, jelly, or spreadable cream cheese on the bread. Roll up the bread from the bottom to the top. Slice the roll into four or five sections. Secure each section with a toothpick.

Celebration Cupcakes

Celebrate any special occasion with these tasty cupcakes. Give each child a plain cupcake. Have her use a plastic knife to spread frosting on it. Then let her decorate the cupcake with tube icing, candy sprinkles, cookie crumbs, or small candies.

100-Piece Snack

Make this snack to celebrate the 100th day of school. To prepare, ask ten parents to each send in one of the following snack foods: peanuts, CheeriOs® cereal, Crispix® cereal, M&M's®, pretzels, cheese crackers, Reese's Pieces®, popcorn, raisins, and miniature marshmallows. Place each snack in a separate bowl. Then give each child a plastic sandwich bag. Have him place ten pieces of each snack into his bag to create a 100-piece snack.

Snack On A Straw

Give each child in a small group a plastic stirring straw and small container of Froot Loops® cereal. Tell her to create a pattern by sliding the cereal on the straw. Then let her eat the cereal for a snack.

Peanut Butter Spider

How about a snack of sticky spiders? Prepare the following recipe prior to the activity:

> 2 cups nonfat dry milk
> 2 cups peanut butter
> 4 tablespoons honey

Mix together the dry milk and peanut butter. Add the honey and stir well. Roll into two-inch balls.

Give each child in a small group a paper plate and a two-inch ball of the peanut butter mixture. Have him divide the ball into two parts and roll each one into a separate ball. Put the two balls together on the paper plate to create the spider's head and body. Then place two chocolate chips in the head to make the eyes. Insert eight pretzel sticks in the spider's body to make the legs. Eat and enjoy!

Buried Cookies

Your students will "dig" this delightful treat! Pour two cups of cold milk into a one-quart shaker. Add a small package of instant pudding. Place the lid securely on the container and shake hard for 45 seconds. Allow the pudding to thicken for five minutes. Have each child in a small group crumble two cookies into a small bowl. Then have her spoon some pudding over the cookie crumbs. Dig in!

Rabbit Food

Celebrate the coming of spring with food fit for a rabbit! For this activity you will need carrots, celery, prepared vegetable dip, vegetable peelers, serrated plastic knives, cutting boards, and paper plates. Place the items on a table in a learning center. Have the children wash the vegetables, then use vegetable peelers to peel the carrots. Use plastic knives to slice the carrots and celery. Place a small amount of vegetable dip and carrot and celery slices on a plate for each child. Have the children dunk the vegetable slices in the dip and nibble away!

Fruit Kabob

Let each child create a Fruit Kabob by sliding the following fruit onto a wooden skewer: strawberry, banana slice, orange section, apple slice, and grape. Have students slide the fruits back off the skewer to enjoy this healthy snack. (Caution students NOT to put skewers in their mouths!)

Ice Cream Sandwich

This cool sandwich treat will delight your youngsters. Give each child two large, soft cookies. Have her use a plastic knife to spread a thin layer of peanut butter on one side of both cookies. Shake candy sprinkles on one cookie. Place a scoop of ice cream on the other cookie. Top the ice cream with the sprinkled cookie to make a sandwich.

WATER AND SAND PLAY

Wash Day

Set up a laundry center in your classroom with a clothesline, clothespins, mild detergent, doll clothes, a washboard, and two tubs of water. Pour a small amount of detergent into one tub and stir. Let the children in the center use the washboard to wash the doll clothes in the soapy water. Then rinse the clothes in the tub of clear water. Wring out the clothes and hang them on the clothesline to dry.

Pouring

Give each child in a learning center a tray and two measuring cups. Have her fill one cup with buttons. Then tell her to pour the buttons into the other cup. If she can pour the buttons without spilling them, have her repeat the process with smaller objects such as dried beans. Finally let her pour water from one cup to the other.

Fun With Sponges

Place two bowls and a garlic press on a tray. Fill one bowl with water. Place several sponge pieces in the water-filled bowl. Then have a child use the garlic press to squeeze the water from a sponge piece into the empty bowl. Have him repeat the procedure with the remaining sponge pieces.

Sand Trays

Collect several shoebox lids. Fill each one half-full with sand. Give a lid to each child in a small group. Tell him to use his finger or a wooden dowel to draw shapes or write letters or numbers in the sand.

Scoop And Count

Your children will have a ball with this water table activity. Fill a water table with several inches of water. Place a number of Ping-Pong® balls in the water. Give each child in a small group a fishnet and a bucket. Have him scoop the balls from the water with the fishnet and place them in his bucket. At the conclusion of the activity, count the number of Ping-Pong balls in each child's bucket.

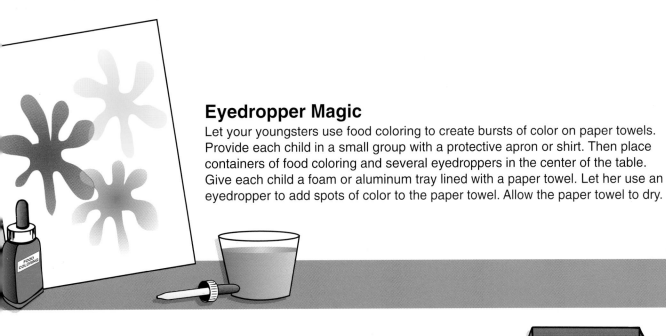

Eyedropper Magic

Let your youngsters use food coloring to create bursts of color on paper towels. Provide each child in a small group with a protective apron or shirt. Then place containers of food coloring and several eyedroppers in the center of the table. Give each child a foam or aluminum tray lined with a paper towel. Let her use an eyedropper to add spots of color to the paper towel. Allow the paper towel to dry.

Measuring With Rice

Fill a sand table with several inches of rice. Have a small group of children use spoons, funnels, and various-sized plastic containers to pour and measure the rice.

Walnut Boats

Each child will enjoy creating and floating her own walnut boat. Give her one-half of a walnut shell. Have her press a small ball of clay into the shell. Then cut a small sail from construction paper. Glue one end of a toothpick to the back of the sail and allow the glue to dry. Insert the other end of the toothpick into the clay and the boat is ready to sail in a water table.

Egg Beater Bubbles

Round and round the egg beater goes, higher and higher the soap bubbles grow! To prepare, give each child in a small group a container of soapy water and an egg beater with a crank handle. Then set an egg timer for one minute. Have each child use the egg beater to beat the soapy water. Compare the amount of bubbles produced by each child.

Rhythm Instruments

Have each child create one of the rhythm instruments below. Then let the children play their instruments along with recordings of their favorite tunes.

Shaker: Use a funnel to pour a handful of dried beans into a plastic half-gallon jug. Replace the lid and shake.

Rattle: Place several jingle bells inside a plastic jar. Replace the lid and shake.

Rhythm Plate: Fold a paper plate in half. Place a handful of rice inside the folded plate and staple shut. Shake to play.

Musical Coloring

Give each child two sheets of white paper and crayons. Then have him listen to a selection of classical music while coloring on one sheet of paper. Repeat the activity with the other sheet of paper, using a selection of rock or jazz music. Then have him compare and contrast his art work.

Sock Beanbags

To prepare, place a bowl of dried beans, a scoop, and several clean socks on a table. Let each child in a small group choose a sock. Have her use the scoop to partially fill the sock with dried beans. Tie a knot in the top. Then use the sock beanbags with your favorite recording of beanbag activities.

Sound Glasses

Children will enjoy experimenting with musical sound glasses. Place identical glasses, a container of water, and a metal spoon in a center. Have the children pour a different amount of water into each glass. Strike the glasses with the spoon and listen to the sounds. Ask children to arrange the glasses by sound from the lowest to the highest pitch. Then have them play sound patterns or simple tunes.

Manual Alphabet

Teach your youngsters to sign the ABCs while singing "The Alphabet Song." To aid their memory, post a picture of each hand signal above the corresponding letter on the classroom alphabet chart and give each child a copy of the reproducible on page 89 to take home.

Hand Games

Clapping Patterns:
Clap your hands several times. Have your students listen for the number of sounds. Then have them clap their hands to show how many times they heard the sound. Vary the activity by demonstrating a simple clapping pattern. Ask the children to repeat it.

Fingerplay Fun:
Divide your class into several small groups. Teach each group a different selection from among your favorite fingerplays. Then have each group teach its fingerplay to the other class members.

Motion Music:
Obtain recordings of several traditional songs such as "Eensy Weensy Spider", "Where Is Thumbkin?", and "Little Cabin In The Wood." As you play each song, sing along with the music and demonstrate the accompanying hand motions. Then re-play the song and have your students join in the fun!

Action Stories

Before reading a familiar fairy tale such as "The Three Little Pigs" or "The Three Bears," assign specific sounds and hand motions to certain characters or actions in the story. Have your youngsters make the sounds and hand motions at the appropriate points in the story.

73

MANIPULATIVE PLAY

Lacing Cards

These durable lacing cards will be "sew" fun for your students! Prepare lacing cards by gluing individual greeting cards shut. Laminate the cards. Use a hole puncher to punch holes around the perimeter of each card. Tie one end of a shoelace in one of the holes. Then let each child in a small group choose a card and lace the shoelace through the remaining holes.

Play Dough Mats

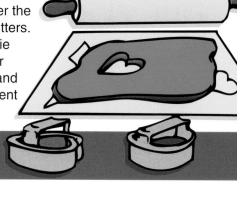

To prepare individual play dough mats, place a cookie cutter on a sheet of 12" x 18" construction paper. Trace around the cookie cutter with a pencil to create a shape. Remove the cookie cutter from the paper and trace over the pencil outline with a marker. Repeat the procedure with other cookie cutters. Laminate the mats for durability. Then place the play dough mats, cookie cutters, and play dough in a learning center. Let each child in the center choose a mat. Then have him roll out the play dough with a rolling pin and use the cookie cutters to cut out the appropriate shapes. Then the student matches the play dough shapes with those on the mat.

Greeting Card Puzzles

To prepare the puzzles, collect several used greeting cards. Cut the front flap off each card. Discard the back flap. Then cut the front flap into three pieces to make a puzzle. Repeat the procedure with the remaining cards. Place all the puzzle pieces into one container. Place the container in a learning center. Let the children put the puzzle pieces together to re-create the greeting card pictures.

Sorting With Tongs

Pour a bag of colored cotton balls into a large bowl. Tell a child to use a pair of pincer-style tongs to sort the cotton balls by color onto individual paper plates.

Nuts, Bolts, And Washers

Place a variety of nuts, bolts, and washers in a tub. Let pairs of children play with the objects by placing the nuts and washers on the bolts.

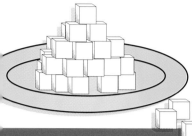

Sugar-Cube Igloo

Let youngsters use sugar cubes to build original igloos. Place paper plates and a container of sugar cubes in a learning center. Have each child in a small group use the sugar cubes to build an igloo on a paper plate foundation. Afterwards replace the materials for another group of children.

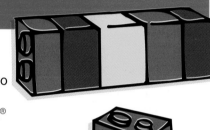

Pattern Cards

Make several copies of the grid on page 90. Color the rectangles in each grid to represent a different pattern. Laminate the grids for durability. Then have each child in a small group choose a grid card and duplicate the pattern using Unifix® cubes or DUPLO® blocks. Let children exchange cards and repeat the activity.

Unweaving

Give each child a small square of fabric, such as burlap, which can be easily unwoven. Have her completely unweave the fabric with her fingers.

Sorting Banks

Collect several glass jars with lids. Make a hole in each lid to create a bank. Tape a different coin on the front of each bank. Place banks and a container of coins in a learning center. Have the children sort the coins by dropping them into the appropriate banks.

Magnetic Board

Place magnetic alphabet letters in random order on a magnetic board. Have a child put the letters in the correct order or use them to spell his name.

Stencils

Create sturdy, inexpensive stencils by using a craft knife to cut simple shapes in old plastic lids. Place the stencils, paper, and colored pencils in a center. Let a small group of children use the materials to create original drawings.

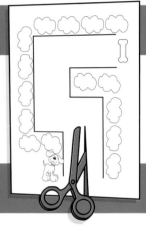

Path Cutting

Supply each child with a copy of page 91. Tell him to help the dog find its bone. Have him use scissors to cut on the center of the path beginning at the X and ending at the bone. Tell him not to let his scissors stray into the bushes.

Containers And Lids

Place a variety of plastic containers and lids on a table in a learning center. Have the children in the center place the lids on the matching containers. Then remove the lids for the next group of children.

Stringing Beads

Place shoelaces and a container of different-sized beads in a learning center. Have the children string the beads on the shoelaces in various patterns, by color, shape, or size.

Snap, Buckle, Zip

Collect several items that have snaps, buckles, or zippers such as belts, purses, wallets, backpacks, or shoes. Let the children practice fastening and unfastening each item.

Twirling Toy

A button and a string can provide your children with old-fashioned fun while strengthening small motor muscles. Provide each child with a large button and a 12-inch piece of string. Have him thread the string through a buttonhole. Next have him wrap the ends of the string around his index fingers as shown. Tell him to hold the left side of the string still and rotate the right side three times. Then have him pull both ends of the string tight and watch the button twirl.

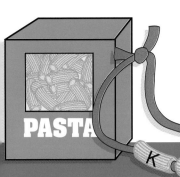

Ziti Words

Purchase a box of ziti pasta. Use a marker to print a different letter on each piece of ziti. Place the ziti in a container. Then have each child in a small group string the ziti on a shoelace to spell her name or simple sight words.

Flannelboard Fun

Place a flannelboard and several felt flannelboard pieces in a learning center. Have the youngsters sort the pieces by color, kind, or shape on the flannelboard.

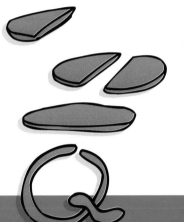

Clay Play

Supply each child in a small group with a piece of clay. Then give directions similar to those printed below. Model each step with a piece of clay.

1. Squeeze the clay in your left hand and count to ten.
2. Squeeze the clay in your right hand and count to ten.
3. Roll the clay into a ball.
4. Flatten the ball into a pancake.
5. Divide the pancake into two parts.
6. Roll each part into a line.
7. Use the two lines to make a letter of the alphabet.

Let It Snow!

Let your children use paper scraps to create a snowstorm in your classroom. Give each child a white sheet of paper. Have her cut the paper into small pieces to make a snow pile. When the cutting is complete, tell your youngsters to scoop up the snow piles in their hands and stand together in an open area of the classroom. Then on the count of three, have them toss the paper flakes into the air and shout, "Let it snow!" Finally tell the children to pretend they are snowplows. Have them collect the paper snow and dump it into the wastebasket.

Blocks

Use a strip of masking tape to make a trail on the classroom floor. Let a small group of children set up a line of building blocks on the trail, standing the blocks on end. Knock over the first block and watch as the others fall like dominoes. To vary the activity, set up two trails of building blocks and have the children predict which one will fall down first.

GAME PLANS

Liter-Bottle Bowling

Give each child in a small group a plastic liter bottle. Have her use a measuring cup and a funnel to fill the base of the bottle with sand at the sand table. Secure the cap. Then set up a bowling alley using the liter-bottle pins. Let the children use a basketball to knock down the pins.

Toothpick Pickup

Place a container of colored toothpicks between a pair of students. Have one child try to pick up two toothpicks between his thumb and index finger. Then let the second child try. The child who picks up exactly two toothpicks may keep them. Repeat the activity, gradually increasing the number of toothpicks to be picked up each time. At the conclusion of the activity, the child with the most toothpicks is the winner.

Slam Dunk

Turn cleanup time into a game of "slam dunk!" After a paper-cutting activity, place wastebaskets around the classroom in convenient locations. Then have each child pick up paper scraps, crumple them into balls, and toss the balls into the nearest wastebasket. Tell her to count the number of paper balls she gets into the wastebasket on the first try.

Beanbag Pass

Have your students form a tight circle, shoulder to shoulder, either standing or sitting. Tell them to place their hands behind their backs. Designate one child as the starter. Place a beanbag in his hands. Then play a familiar song to set the pace and have the children pass the beanbag around the circle until the music stops. If the beanbag is dropped, return it to the starter and begin again.

Card Games

Purchase several inexpensive card games such as Old Maid, Fish, MY FIRST UNO® Card Game, and the Original Memory® Game. Let small groups of children play the games to strengthen fine-motor muscles and thinking skills.

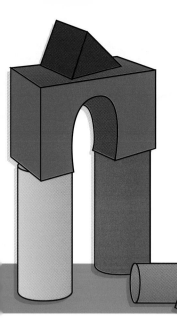

Commercial Games

Commercial games can be played indoors when the weather does not permit your class to go outside. Purchase several games that strengthen fine-motor muscles such as Barrel Of Monkeys®, Super Block Head!®, Ants In The Pants®, Cootie®, Don't Spill The Beans®, and Trouble®. Place each game in a different center for small groups to play.

Musical Cotton Balls

Put a new twist on an old game. Have your students sit in a circle on the floor. Give each one a clothespin. Place a cotton ball on the floor in front of one child. Tell him to pick up the cotton ball with his clothespin. Next have him use the clothespin to place the cotton ball in front of the person to his left. Begin the music and have the children pass the cotton ball around the circle in a similar fashion. When the music stops, the child holding the cotton ball is out of the game. Play ends when one child is left. (To lessen the competitive nature of the game, give each child a sticker as he exits the circle.)

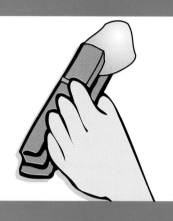

Magic Hand

Place a 4" x 4" piece of paper on a table in front of each child in a small group. Tell him to place one hand behind his back. Then have him pick up the paper with his free hand. Ask him to make the paper disappear by crumpling it into a small ball. Instruct him not to touch his body or the table with his magic hand. Once the paper has disappeared, tell him to place the paper ball on the table. Have him smooth it out with both hands. Then repeat the procedure with the other hand. To vary the activity, let the children race to see who can make the paper disappear first.

Water Bucket Relay

Divide your class into teams of four to six youngsters. Have each team stand in a straight line. Give each team member a plastic cup. Place a bucket of water at the beginning of each line and an empty bucket at the end of the line. Then instruct the first child in each line to dip her cup into the bucket of water and fill it. Have her turn to the next child in line and pour the water from her cup into his cup. Have the remaining team members repeat the process until the last child in line empties his cup into the empty bucket. Repeat the relay activity five times. Then measure the water collected in each bucket to determine the winning team.

ART ADVENTURES

Magic Board Rubbings

These magic board rubbings will delight and amaze your students. Prepare magic boards by gluing scraps of sandpaper, burlap, corrugated cardboard, coins, puzzle pieces, keys, and bent pipe cleaners on cardboard squares. Allow the glue to dry. Then cover each board with paper and tape it to the back. Have a child rub the paper with the side of an unwrapped crayon. The impression of the objects will appear on the paper. When complete, take the paper off the magic board and trim around the edges. The magic boards may be used again by rewrapping with clean paper.

Toothpick Sculpture

Let each child create an abstract sculpture using toothpicks and foam packing pieces. Place a container of colored toothpicks and a container of foam packing pieces in a center. Tell each child to create an individual sculpture by connecting packing pieces with the toothpicks.

Completing Shapes

Give each child a copy of the reproducible on page 92. Have her complete the pictures of the shapes and color as desired.

Spiderweb Weaving

Cut a six-inch circle from black poster board for each child. Cut eight, 1/2-inch slits around the circumference of the circle as shown. Attach a long piece of white string to the back center of the circle with tape. Let a child weave the string back and forth through the slits in the circle to create a spiderweb. When complete, tape the end of the string to the back of the circle. Then glue a plastic spider or insect to the front of the web.

Christmas Garland

This festive garland will brighten your classroom during the Christmas season. Obtain a bag of small pretzels, a long strand of red ribbon, and two large safety pins. Demonstrate how to thread the ribbon through the top two holes of a pretzel. Secure the short end of the ribbon with a safety pin. Then let a child repeat the procedure with the remaining pretzels. Secure the other end of the ribbon with the second safety pin. Hang the completed garland on a Christmas tree or above a chalkboard.

Wet-On-Wet

Your children will learn about colors as they experiment with watercolor paint. To prepare, cover a table with newspapers. Place three or four aluminum trays on the table. Set a sheet of watercolor paper in each tray. Place containers of red, blue, and yellow watercolor paint in the center of the table. Then have a child stand at each tray. Let her use a spray bottle of clean water to wet the paper thoroughly. (There should be a little water standing in the tray.) Next dip a wet paintbrush in a container of paint and touch the brush to the paper. (The color will burst on the paper.) Repeat the procedure with the other colors using clean, wet paintbrushes. Carefully remove the paper from the tray and let dry. Mount each painting on a larger sheet of construction paper to create a frame.

Mirror Drawing

Give each child a copy of page 93. Have her complete the picture of the butterfly. Then let her color the picture.

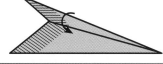

Origami Flower

These decorative paper flowers will add a splash of color to your classroom. Have each child fold a colorful paper napkin in half to form a triangle. Make sure the fold is at the bottom. Then fold the center point down as shown. Cut as indicated. The napkin will be a circular shape. Pinch the center of the circle and twist to create a flower. Wrap one end of a pipe cleaner around the twisted end of the flower to make the stem. Place the completed flowers in a vase to create an attractive bouquet.

Rainbow Tracing

Your youngsters will have fun turning black and white shapes into rainbow shapes. Supply each child with a copy of page 94. Have her use three differently colored crayons to trace around each shape as shown (one crayon at a time).

Christmas Oranges

These fragrant Christmas oranges will fill your classroom with the wonderful smell of the holiday season. Give each child an orange and several whole cloves. Have her push the end of each clove through the orange peel. Then assist students in using a straight pin to attach a red or green bow to the top of the orange. Display the Christmas oranges in a large glass bowl.

Giraffe Puzzle

Duplicate page 95 on yellow construction paper for each child. Have him cut out the shapes and glue them on a sheet of blue construction paper as shown. Allow the glue to dry. Use a marker to draw the eye, mouth, and nose. Use a brown crayon to add spots.

Yarn Zoo

To prepare for this activity, obtain a foam meat tray for each child. Make 1/2-inch cuts in each tray as shown. Place the meat trays, pictures of zoo animals, yarn, tape, and glue in a learning center. Let each child choose a picture and glue it on the front of a tray. Secure a piece of yarn to the back of the tray with tape. Then wrap the yarn around the tray, pulling the yarn through the cuts. Secure the end of the yarn to the back of the tray when the weaving is complete.

Forsythia Branches

Supply each child in a small group with a 12" x 18" sheet of white construction paper, a paintbrush, and a cotton swab. Have her dip the paintbrush into a container of brown paint and paint a branch on her paper. Next have her dip the cotton swab in green paint and print leaves on the branches. Finally let her dip her finger in yellow paint to create forsythia blooms.

Number People

Give each child a pipe cleaner and a sheet of white paper. Have him bend the pipe cleaner into the shape of a number. Glue the pipe cleaner onto the paper. Place a heavy book on the pipe-cleaner number until the glue dries. Then use markers or crayons to draw the features and create a unique "number person."

Wood Scrap Art

Obtain several wood scraps from a woodworker or homebuilder. Place the wood scraps, paper, colored pencils, and crayons in a learning center. Let each child choose a scrap of wood. Have him use a colored pencil to trace the shape on the paper. Then color the shape with a crayon. Repeat the procedure with other wood scraps. Children may choose to create an abstract work of art or an object such as a rocket, car, house, or flower.

Cardboard Pizza

Cut a nine-inch circle from cardboard for each child. Have her paint the circle with red tempera paint to represent tomato sauce. While the paint is wet, sprinkle it with cornmeal to represent cheese. Allow the cornmeal to set for one minute. Then shake off the excess. Next dip a carrot (cut crosswise) in the red paint and use it to print pepperoni slices on the cardboard pizza.

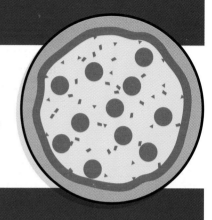

Sock Puppet Theater

Ask each child to bring a clean, adult-sized sock from home. Have him use materials such as yarn, fabric scraps, buttons, sequins, felt, rickrack, pipe cleaners, etc., to decorate the sock and make a puppet. Then let small groups of children use their completed puppets to put on puppet shows.

Movement Strokes

Tape a large sheet of paper to the chalkboard or wall. Give each child a sheet of paper and a crayon. Tell your students to follow your directions and make strokes on their papers to represent how different things move. Instruct them to listen carefully and make each stroke after you demonstrate it. While you draw, give the following directions:

1. Let your crayon hop like a rabbit.

2. Let your crayon roll like a wave.

3. Let your crayon bounce like a ball.

4. Let your crayon march like a soldier.

5. Let your crayon fly like a bee.

6. Let your crayon spin like a top.

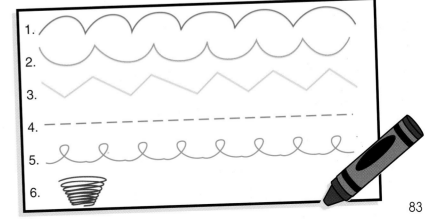

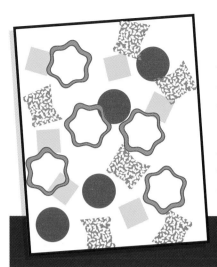

Printing

To prepare for this activity, collect an assortment of materials that can be used to print shapes. Materials may include cardboard tubes, blocks, clothespins, crumpled paper, pencil erasers, spools, and vegetable slices. Place the printing materials, tempera paint, and 12" x 18" sheets of construction paper in a learning center. Ask each child to choose an object and dip it in a container of tempera paint. Then tell him to press the object on a sheet of paper to create an interesting shape. Have him repeat the process until the paper is covered. Allow the paint to dry.

Clouds

Take your students outside to observe clouds. Ask them to describe any shapes they see in the cloud formations. Then return to the classroom and give each child a sheet of blue construction paper, a crumpled paper towel, and a container of slightly thinned white tempera paint. Demonstrate how to make cloud shapes by dipping the paper towel in the white paint and pressing it on the paper. Turn the paper towel each time you make a print so every cloud will look different. Scatter the clouds around the paper, allowing some of the blue to show through. After students have created their own paintings, have them describe any shapes they may see in their clouds. When the paintings are dry, have each child use markers and crayons to draw an object such as a bird, airplane, rainbow, sun, or rocket in the clouds.

Puffy Fish

Give each child a paper lunch bag and a sheet of newspaper. Tell him to tear the newspaper into wide strips and crumple them into balls. Have him stuff the bag with the paper balls. Then twist a twist tie or rubber band around the bag opening to create a tail. Sponge-paint the bag with tempera paint to make the scales. While the paint is drying, cut or tear three fins, two eyes, and a mouth from construction-paper scraps. Glue the fins, eyes, and mouth to the puffy fish as shown.

Mosaic

Duplicate the reproducible on page 90 on several sheets of colored construction paper. Place the colored paper, scissors, glue, and sheets of white construction paper in a learning center. Let each child choose two or three sheets of colored paper. Have her cut on the black lines to create several squares. Tell her to arrange the squares on a sheet of white construction paper in the shape of an object such as a flower, house, or car. Then glue each square to the paper.

Pushpin Art

Give each child a copy of the sun pattern on page 96. Have her place the copy over a sheet of yellow construction paper. Secure the papers with paper clips and place on a carpeted surface. Use a pushpin to punch a hole through each dot. When complete, remove the clips and the sun reproducible. Then tape the yellow paper to a window. The light will shine through the holes, creating a shimmering sun.

Paper Recycling

Recycle old newspapers into beautiful works of art! Give each child a newspaper section and ask her to tear it into small pieces. Have the children place their newspaper pieces into a large container. Pour water over the newspaper until it is covered. Allow the paper to soak overnight, and then use a hand mixer to beat the paper into mush. (Add more water if needed.) Place a piece of screen in a sunny area outside. Set several embroidery hoops on the screen. Pour the paper mush into the hoops and allow it to dry in the sun. Remove the dried paper circles from the hoops. Then let the children use tempera paint to create attractive designs on the circles.

Clay Beads

Give each child in a small group a piece of air-dry modeling compound. Demonstrate how to divide the compound into small pieces. Roll each piece into a ball. Use a drinking straw or nail to make a hole through each ball. Have each child follow your example to make four or five beads. Allow the beads to dry. Then have him paint his beads with colored tempera paints and let dry. String the beads on a ribbon and tie the ends together to make a necklace.

String Painting

Your students will enjoy creating attractive abstract paintings using a comb and a piece of string. To prepare for the activity, give each child in a small group a comb, a piece of string, and a sheet of finger-paint paper. Have her lace one end of the string through several of the comb's teeth. Then place a nickel-sized drop of red finger paint on the paper. Instruct the child to hold the comb above the paper so the string touches the paint. Have her use the comb to guide the string through the paint and create a design on the paper. Repeat the procedure with drops of blue and yellow finger paint.

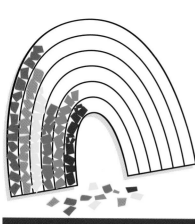

Paper Rainbow

To prepare for this activity, draw a rainbow shape on a large sheet of white paper and cut it out. Then use a marker to divide the rainbow into six sections. Label the sections as follows: red, orange, yellow, green, blue, and purple. Next place the paper rainbow, sheets of differently colored construction paper, and glue in a learning center. Have a small group of children tear the construction paper into small pieces and glue to the appropriate sections. Repeat the activity with other small groups until the rainbow is complete. Use the rainbow as a door decoration or part of a bulletin-board display.

Kitchen Art

Your children can create colorful collages using ordinary kitchen gadgets. Collect an assortment of gadgets such as graters, potato mashers, biscuit cutters, spatulas, cookie cutters, plastic forks, and drinking straws. Tell each child in a small group to use a sheet of copy paper and a crayon to create rubbings of the graters. Next have him choose several other kitchen gadgets. Tell him to dip each one in tempera paint and use it to print on a sheet of white construction paper. Allow the paint to dry, Then cut out the rubbings and the printed shapes. Glue them to a 12" x 18" sheet of colored construction paper to create a collage.

Tracing Shadows

Tape a sheet of paper to the wall. Then hang a stencil from a fixed point in front of the paper. Have one child shine a flashlight on the stencil so it casts a shadow on the paper. Have another child trace the shadow. Then ask the children to change positions and repeat the activity. Afterwards let the children color their shapes. When every child has completed a shadow tracing, mount the shapes on a large sheet of paper to make a shadow collage.

Holiday Hats

Let each child decorate a hat for a recent or upcoming holiday. Supply each child with a newspaper section. Have her turn the newspaper horizontally. Fold the top two corners to the center. Fold the two bottom corners as shown. Then fold the front flap up. Turn the newspaper over and repeat with the other flap. Staple as shown. Then decorate the hat with a variety of materials such as sequins, feathers, and streamers in appropriate colors for the chosen holiday.

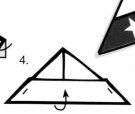

1.

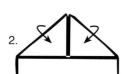
2.

3.

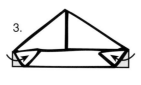
4.

TRINKETS AND TREASURES

Potpourri

This fragrant potpourri will be a cherished Christmas or Mother's Day gift. Give each child a plastic freezer bag. Have her place broken cinnamon sticks, whole cloves, and whole allspice in the bag and seal. Let her use a rolling pin to crush the spices. Shake gently to mix. Then pour the potpourri into a decorative cloth bag and tie with a ribbon.

Rainbow Wreath

To prepare, cut a six-inch wreath shape from tagboard for each child. (Or cut out the center of a six-inch paper plate.) Then have her crumple a colorful supply of 2" x 2" squares of tissue paper into balls. Glue the balls on the wreath shape. Allow the glue to dry. Then use three colors of ribbon to create a bow at the top of the wreath.

Jigsaw Magnet

Give each child four or five small cardboard puzzle pieces. Have him paint each piece with acrylic paint and allow the paint to dry. Then glue the puzzle pieces together so they overlap. Let the glue dry. Next decorate the puzzle pieces with sequins and glitter and allow the glue to dry. Then attach a magnetic strip to the back to complete the jigsaw magnet.

Bookmark

Here's a fun gift for Mom, Dad, or a class of "buddy readers!" Give each child a 2" x 7" strip of tagboard. Let him use a hole puncher to make a hole in one end. Next have him glue a picture of himself below the hole. Let him use markers to decorate the front and back of the bookmark. Laminate the bookmark for durability and repunch the hole. Then fold a six-inch piece of yarn in half. Thread the yarn through the hole and tie the ends as shown.

Patchwork Placemats

Ask your children to bring fabric scraps from home. Place the fabric scraps, 12" x 18" sheets of construction paper, and glue in a learning center. Let each child choose several fabric scraps. Have her glue the scraps to a sheet of construction paper as shown. Allow the glue to dry. Then laminate the placemat for durability.

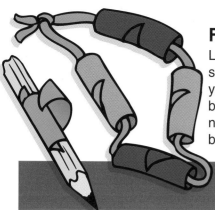

Friendship Bracelet

Let each child make a friendship bracelet for a special friend. To prepare, cut several long, thin triangles from magazine pages. Place the triangles, pencils, yarn, and glue on a table in a learning center. Demonstrate how to make a paper bead by rolling a triangle around a pencil starting with the wide end. Glue the narrow end down and allow to dry. Have each child make four or five similar beads. Then string the beads on a strand of yarn and tie to create a bracelet.

Stick Pin

Children will have fun creating colorful pins from wooden craft sticks. Have each child glue colored sequins to the front of a craft stick in a decorative design. Allow the glue to dry. Have an adult use a hot glue gun to attach a large safety pin to the back of the craft stick.

Burlap Sewing

To prepare for this activity, cut a piece of burlap in a square for each child in a small group. Use a piece of chalk to draw a simple outline such as a sun, flower, turtle, star, fish, or tree on each burlap square. Next give each child a large needle threaded with yarn. Let him push the needle up from the bottom side of the fabric, then down, creating stitches around the chalk outline as shown.

Finger Bow

These attractive bows may be used to decorate packages or potted plants. Divide the class into pairs. Supply each child with a 12-inch piece of narrow ribbon and a twist-tie. Have one partner extend and spread the index finger and middle finger on one hand. Instruct the other child to wrap the ribbon around the spread fingers. Then have him twist the tie around the center of the ribbon. Remove the ribbon from the partner's fingers and twist the tie again to tighten. Fluff the bow by gently pulling the loops apart.

Tile Flower

Purchase a ceramic tile for each child from a home improvement store. Place the tiles, paintbrushes, and containers of yellow, blue, and green acrylic paint on a table for a small group. Have each child dip a paintbrush in the yellow paint and paint a yellow circle in the center of her tile. Next have her dip her index finger in the blue paint and print the petals around the yellow center. Then tell her to dip a paintbrush in the green paint and create the stem and leaves. Allow the paint to dry. Have an adult spray the tile with a fixative. Use a marker to print the child's name and the date on the back of the tile. Then attach felt circles around the perimeter on the back.

THE MANUAL ALPHABET

A   B   C   D   E   F   G

H   I   J   K   L   M

  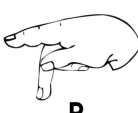   

N   O   P   Q   R   S

     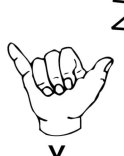 

T   U   V   W   X   Y   Z

Patterns

Use with the "Pattern Cards" activity on page 75.

Use with the "Mosaic" activity on page 84.

X

Note To The Teacher: Use with the "Path Cutting" activity on page 76.

Name _____

Completing shapes

circle

rectangle

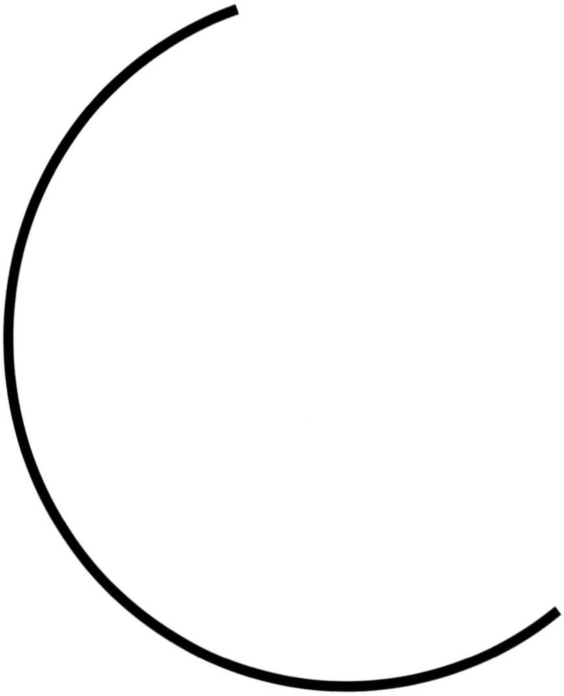

square

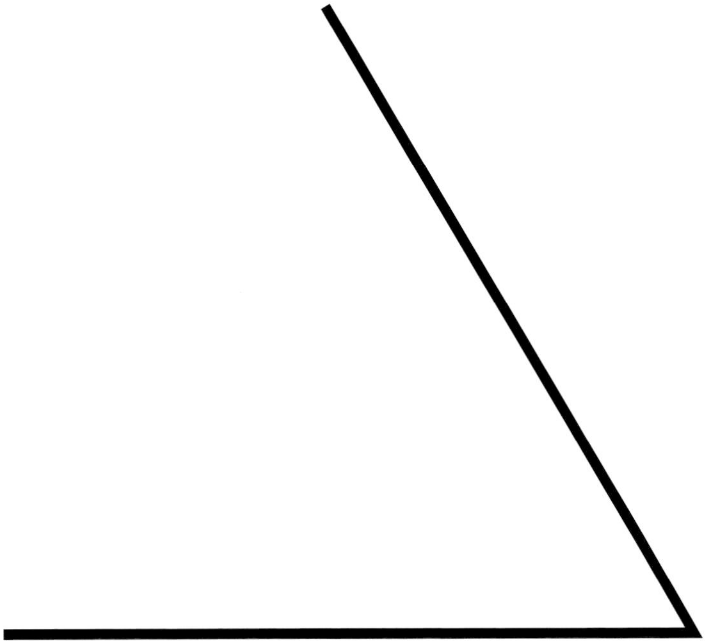

triangle

©1995 The Education Center, Inc. • *Trace & Lace, Color & Paste* • TEC906

92   **Note To The Teacher:** Use with the "Completing Shapes" activity on page 80.

Note To The Teacher: Use with the "Mirror Drawing" activity on page 81.

Note To The Teacher: Use with the "Rainbow Tracing" activity on page 81.